THE DISCRETE
MAXIMUM PRINCIPLE

a study of multistage
systems optimization

THE DISCRETE

MAXIMUM PRINCIPLE

a study of multistage systems optimization

LIANG-TSENG FAN

Professor, Department of Chemical Engineering
Kansas State University, Manhattan, Kansas

CHIU-SEN WANG

Research Assistant, Department of Chemical Engineering
Kansas State University, Manhattan, Kansas

John Wiley & Sons, Inc., New York · London · Sydney

Preface

This monograph presents the results of the authors' attempt to apply Pontryagin's maximum principle to the optimization of multistage decision processes. The ultimate motivation is to study the multistage optimization problems from a unified point of view. In order to do so, multistage decision processes are analyzed and classified according to their topological structure and dimensionality. A brief survey of the common methods of optimization is then presented so that the readers may be aware of the present status of the optimization techniques. A version of the discrete maximum principle suitable for the optimization of simple feedback processes is then developed in Chapter 3 and its application illustrated in the subsequent three chapters. The problems are selected from various fields of engineering and economics, spanning from the optimal design of chemical reactors and step rockets to transportation problems. Chapter 7 is a brief presentation of a generalized version of the discrete maximum principle suitable for the optimization of topologically complex multistage processes. General remarks on the maximum principle and dynamic programming are made in the concluding chapter. In order to make the exposition more nearly self-contained, some basic notions of Pontryagin's maximum principle and dynamic programming are described in the Appendices. Appendix 4 is devoted to some preliminary results on the sufficiency and necessity of the optimum conditions.

It is the desire of the authors to develop and present the discrete maximum principle as a practical tool of optimization. A considerable amount of detail in derivations and solutions of the various methods and problems is given so that the book can be used by practicing "optimizers" as well as the beginning graduate students. Special care was given to maintain uniformity and continuity of presentation and to avoid undue mathematical rigor. In other words, we were mostly concerned with methods and solutions rather than rigorous justification of the conditions

v

under which the methods hold. Often we could base such justification on physical ground and past experiences.

This monograph by no means represents the final account of the development of the discrete maximum principle. We only hope that this will induce and stimulate other workers in the field to undertake further improvement of the method.

We are indebted to our many teachers for their guidance and assistance. In particular, the senior author wishes to mention Professors S. L. Wang, R. C. Taecker, H. V. Fairbanks, W. A. Koehler, and H. A. Davis, and the junior author wishes to acknowledge Professors C. Y. Cheng, and B. G. Kyle. The senior author was introduced to modern mathematical optimization methods by Professors R. Aris, D. R. Rudd, and D. J. Wilde. He, in turn, introduced the junior author to the field.

Several persons contributed problems and in some cases solutions by means of the methods presented in the book. Their names appear in the appropriate references and in The Author Index. Although the monograph includes for the most part original material and development, we were strongly influenced by the writings of Drs. L. S. Pontryagin, R. Bellman, S. Katz, and S. S. L. Chang.

The manuscript was critically reviewed from an economist's point of view by Mr. L. S. Fan, a brother of the senior author, who is an instructor and research fellow at the University of Minnesota. Many of his valuable suggestions are incorporated in the book. The book was also critically reviewed by Professor C. Y. Wen and graduate students, particularly Messrs. S. J. Chen and Y. C. Ko, who took the courses in advanced process design and chemical engineering analysis the last two years.

We appreciate the competent typing of the manuscript by Misses Judy Taylor and Barbara LaBarre. Messrs. Y. C. Lei and R. C. Lin assisted with the proofreading and the indexes and Mrs. W. C. Lin and Mr. K. C. Cheng with the preparation of the figures.

This book probably would never have been completed without the generous support of the Engineering Experiment Station and the Computing Center of Kansas State University. In this connection we would like to thank Professors L. Hobson, D. Nesmith, and S. T. Parker.

Encouragement given to the authors by their colleagues in the Department of Chemical Engineering at Kansas State University, headed by Dr. William H. Honstead, is also acknowledged.

Liang-tseng Fan
Chiu-sen Wang

Department of Chemical Engineering
Kansas State University
April 1964

Contents

1

Introduction

1. THE CONCEPT OF OPTIMIZATION

Human wants are ever increasing as technology advances in producing more products from limited natural and human resources. As resources are being further depleted, the progress in technology has to be speeded up so that the rapidly expanding human wants can be satisfied. Daily activities of individuals, of gigantic enterprises, and, as a matter of fact, the activities of the whole economic system of a country have been based on a simple principle of "optimality." The enduring effort to improve the technology has gradually given rise to the notion of optimization. Optimization is the act of obtaining the best result under given (fixed) conditions. To elaborate this point, individuals try to gain maximum satisfactions with their limited budgets (income), and all productions of industrial concerns are aimed at attaining maximum profit (minimum cost) under existing technological restrictions (constraints).

The act of optimization frequently presents a mathematical problem of such a nature that a certain function of several variables is to be maximized or minimized with some constraints imposed on the variables. Since it is the objective of the optimizer (operator) to operate the system in the best way, such a function representing the performance criterion of a system is called the objective function. It is clear that the maximization or minimization of the objective function leads to the optimization of the system. The optimizer has several variables under his control, which will be called the decision variables. The problem for him is to find the values of decision variables, within the allowed boundary (constraints), which maximize the value of the objective function. Such a sequence of decisions is called an optimal policy.

Optimization is an art which requires the ingenuity and learnedness of the individual involved in carrying it out. However, the past experience of human efforts has resulted in many refined mathematical techniques that assist us in attaining goals of optimization.

The common procedure in optimizing a system is divided into five steps by Cochran [1].

1. Definitions of objective, system boundaries, independent variables, restrictions, and external parameters. This task can be briefly explained. The objective function for business enterprise is usually a profit function using capital expenditure as the decision variable, or it may be a cost function when minimization of cost is the objective. All restrictions, boundary conditions, and external parameters should be clearly defined so that the solution for a system is consistent.

2. Analysis and simplification. This does not need too much elaboration. All situations should be analyzed before any calculation is executed because the act of simplification itself may cut down the enormous cost of calculation and it may be a part of the optimal policy. The simplification may apply to the reduction of insignificant variables and of inferior processes. The simplification may also be accomplished by dividing a process of many variables into a process with several stages (blocks) of few variables.

3. Simulation or mathematization of the objective (response) function. This task of formulating mathematical equations may be theoretical or empirical. Many statistical or computer techniques will help.

4. Verification or checking. Simulation is useless unless the empirical or theoretical equations are tested against the system in reality which is under consideration. The "goodness" or "badness" of equations determines the success or failure of the last step of actual optimization calculation.

These steps depend largely on the individual in charge of optimization. They are not the main topics of our monograph.

5. Optimization-solutions of functions for extrema. This usually requires extensive mathematical analysis. Various optimization techniques are briefly discussed in Section 2.1.*

As previously mentioned, the ceaseless effort in maintaining and improving the welfare of human beings has resulted in the formulation of

---

* The first number indicates the chapter.

these mathematical techniques of optimization. Many of the techniques are applicable to wide fields of human activities.

Many of these activities are stagewise in structure, whereas others are continuous. A stagewise process generally can be described by a system of difference equations; a continuous process is, on the other hand, described by a system of differential equations. Because of the inherent restrictions on human decisions and their execution, many continuous processes are actually carried out stage by stage. Furthermore, a continuous process usually can be approximated by a stagewise process. Thus our task of optimization is to find the values of decision variables at each stage so that the objective function of a multistage process is maximized.

2. MULTISTAGE DECISION PROCESSES

A multistage decision process may be considered as an abstract notion by which a large number of human activities can be represented. A process is either deterministic or stochastic. In this monograph only deterministic cases are treated. Since a multistage decision process is an entity consisting of a finite number of stages, its nature is completely determined by the types of stages from which it is formed and by the ways the stages are interconnected.

A stage may represent any real or abstract entity (for example, a space unit, a time period, or an economic activity) in which a certain transformation takes place. Those variables which are transformed in each stage are called state variables. The desired transformation for the state variables is achieved through manipulation of decision variables which remain or may be considered to remain constant within each stage of the process. The transformation at each stage is completely described by a set of performance equations.

A stage may have any number of entering and leaving streams by which the state variables are transferred into and out of the stage. It is convenient to classify the stages by the number of streams with which they are associated. Four basic types of stages are shown in Fig. 1. A linking stage is a stage with one entering stream and one leaving stream. A stage with one entering stream and several leaving streams is called a separating stage. A combining stage represents a stage which has one leaving stream, but several entering streams. Finally, a stage with several entering streams and several leaving streams is a complex stage.

If a multistage decision process consists entirely of linking stages, it is called a simple process. A complex process is a process containing at least one stage other than the linking stage. Figure 2 shows some of the typical

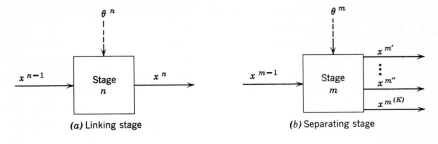

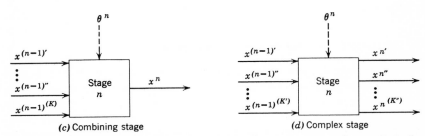

Fig. 1 Four basic types of stage. x represents the state vector; θ represents the decision vector.

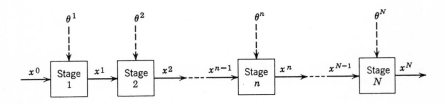

(a) simple process

Fig. 2 Multistage processes. x represents the state vector; θ represents the decision vector.

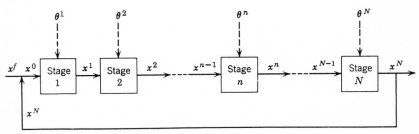

Fig. 2b Simple feedback process.

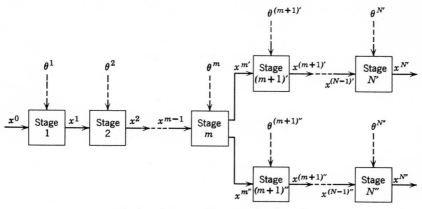

Fig. 2c Process with separating branch.

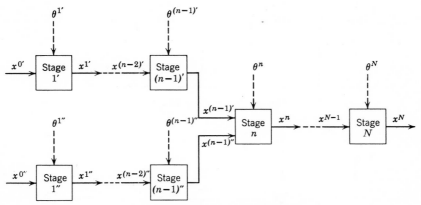

Fig. 2d Process with combining branch.

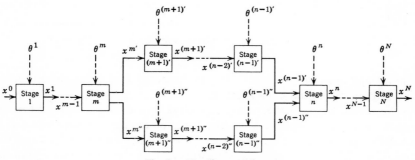

Fig. 2e Feedforward loop.

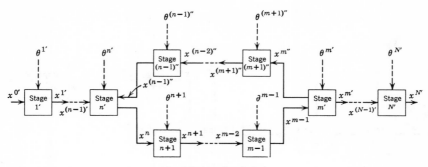

Fig. 2f   Feedback loop.

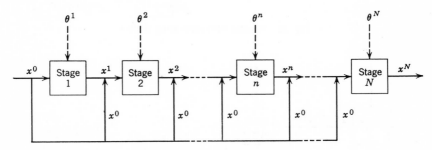

Fig. 2g   Multistream feedforward.

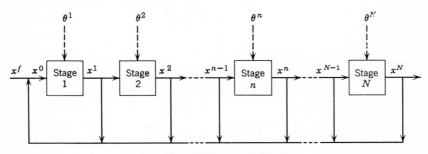

Fig. 2h   Multistream feedback.

multistage decision processes. It may be noted that a process can have more than one initial or final stage.

A process can be further categorized either as a homogeneous or a heterogeneous process depending on the form of the performance equations. A homogeneous process is a process in which the state variables and the decision variables are interrelated by the same set of performance equations

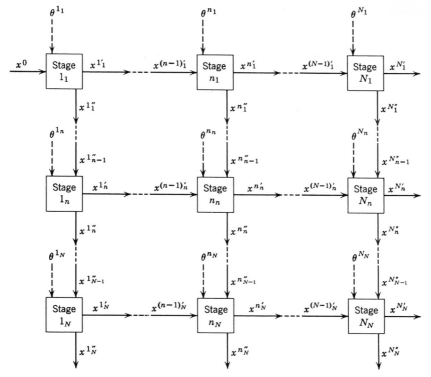

Fig. 2i Network.

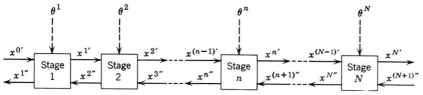

Fig. 2j Countercurrent process.

throughout the process. A process is called heterogeneous if it is not a homogeneous process.

3. MULTISTAGE OPTIMIZATION PROBLEMS

The problem of optimizing a multistage decision process is called a multistage optimization problem. The objective function of the process, which is to be maximized or minimized, can be expressed as a function of the state variables leaving the last stage of the process. Thus a general multistage optimization problem can be stated as follows.

For a process with all the performance equations and the initial and/or final values of some of the state variables given, find the values of the decision variables at each stage, subject to certain constraints, in such a way that the objective function is maximized or minimized.

Let us now consider a few concrete examples of problems of this nature.

Suppose that we have a certain amount of a resource which may represent labor, capital, or a natural resource. The resource can be utilized in a number of different ways. Each of such possible applications is called an activity. As a result of allocating some amount of the resource to an activity, a certain return is obtained. The return depends on the nature of the activity as well as the amount of resource allocated. We may assume that the returns from different activities can be measured in a common unit and that the total return is the sum of the individual returns. A problem that may come to mind is that of distributing the resource in such a manner that the total return is maximized. The problem can be simplified by assuming that the return from any activity is independent of the allocations to the other activities. If each activity is considered as a stage, such a process becomes a simple multistage process, with the amount of resource allocated to each stage serving as the decision variable. Associated with the process are two state variables, the amount of resource left after each allocation and the cumulative return. The objective function is the total return which is represented by one of the state variables leaving the last stage.

One of the common processes employed in the chemical industry is the cross-current extraction process consisting of a number of stages connected in series. A solvent containing a solute passes from stage to stage. At each stage, the solute is extracted from the solvent by the addition of wash water which is immiscible with the solvent. The net profit from the process is the total price of solute extracted minus the total cost of the wash water. The optimization problem is to determine the amount of wash water to be added to each stage so as to maximize the net profit. This is a typical, simple multistage process with each stage representing a space unit. The amount of wash water added at each stage is the decision variable. The concentration of the solute and the cumulative net profit are the two state variables. The objective function is the total net profit which is represented by one of the state variables leaving the last stage. If a portion of the end product is fed back to the first stage, the process becomes a simple feedback process.

Finally, let us consider a chemical reactor in which a catalytic reaction is carried out. The efficiency of the reactor gradually decreases as the catalyst becomes older. Eventually a state is reached in which regeneration or replacement of the catalyst is desired. A problem of great significance is to find the best operating conditions (such as temperature and flow rate) for each day as well as the best time for regenerating or replacing the catalyst in order to obtain the maximum profit. This is also a typical simple process, but the stage in this case is a time period, that is, a day. The operating temperature and the flow rate are the two decision variables. The cumulative flow rate, which characterizes the activity of the catalyst, and the cumulative net profit are considered as the two state variables. The objective function is the total net profit which is represented by one of the state variables leaving the last stage.

REFERENCE

1. Cochran, W. O., "Procedure for Selection of Optimum Conditions," *Chem. Engng. Prog. Symp.*, Series 31, **56,** 88 (1960).

2

Mathematical Optimization Techniques

1. COMMON TECHNIQUES OF OPTIMIZATION

There are many techniques of searching for the extremal value of a function. In this section, we state briefly some of the most frequently used techniques for solving problems of extrema, or commonly called optimization techniques.

a. ***Direct Method of Calculation.*** Once a functional relationship is formulated between a decision variable and an objective function, we can directly calculate the value of the objective function for one fixed decision variable. Whenever the value of the function is increased by using another value of the decision variable, we pick the second value instead of the first. This calculation can be repeated until no more improvement can be made on the value of the objective function.

This method is applicable whenever there is a single decision variable or when there are few variables with limited choices. Whenever the domain of the decision variable increases and/or there is more than one extremal value for the state variable, the task of finding the extremal value becomes inhibitive.

b. ***Classical Differential Calculus Method.*** The problem of maxima and minima has been widely treated in conventional differential calculus (see Reference 1). When the objective function f has as its arguments $x = (x_1, x_2, \ldots, x_n)$, and when its first partial derivatives are continuous, then we can set the partial derivatives of f with respect to x_i equal to zero.

$$\left(\frac{\partial f}{\partial x_i}\right)_{x_r \text{ for } r \neq i} = 0, \qquad i = 1, 2, \ldots, n$$

The values of x_i obtained by solving these n equations simultaneously give the objective function f an extremum. Whether it is maximum or minimum can be determined from the sign and/or magnitude of the second and/or higher derivatives.

When there is no other value greater (smaller) than the value we obtained, we are assured of the maximum (minimum) of the function. The last sentence refers to the unimodality of an extremum.

When the function $f(x_1, x_2, \ldots, x_n) = 0$ is to be solved for extrema under constraints, $g_j(x_1, x_2, \ldots, x_n) = 0$, $(j = 1, 2, \ldots, m; \; m < n)$, we can solve m equations of g and express variables, $x_{n-m+1}, x_{n-m+2}, \ldots, x_n$, in terms of $x_1, x_2, \ldots, x_{n-m}$. Then the function f is partially differentiated with respect to $x_1, x_2, \ldots, x_{n-m}$. The $(n - m)$ partial derivatives are set to zero and solved for $x_1, x_2, \ldots, x_{n-m}$. The rest of the variables, x_{n-m+1}, $x_{n-m+2}, \ldots, x_n$, are then readily obtained from the expression derived from the constraints. However, the Lagrange multiplier method provides a useful tool in solving problems of constrained extrema.

c. **Lagrangian Multiplier Method.** The Lagrangian multiplier method introduces m undetermined coefficients (multipliers), $\lambda_1, \lambda_2, \ldots, \lambda_m$, and makes a composite function, $F = f - \lambda_1 g_1 - \lambda_2 g_2 - \cdots - \lambda_m g_m$. The remaining procedure is to form the system of equations by partially differentiating F with respect to $x_1, x_2, \ldots, x_n$

$$\frac{\partial F}{\partial x_i} = 0, \qquad i = 1, 2, \ldots, n$$

$$g_j(x_1, x_2, \ldots, x_n) = 0, \qquad j = 1, 2, \ldots, m$$

With the preceding $(n + m)$ equations, we can solve for n unknowns of x and m unknowns of λ.

The set, $(x_1, x_2, \ldots, x_n)$, thus obtained is the combination of x which gives the extremal value.

The techniques mentioned apply only to internal extrema. Whenever extrema are located at points of the region of variation, the property of $\partial f / \partial x_i = 0$ generally does not exist. Thus, before any final judgement is passed, we have to evaluate f at the boundary points to see whether it is the real maximum (minimum).

d. **The Calculus of Variations.** Another classical analytical method is the calculus of variations. A typical problem treated by this method is that of finding a function $y = y(x)$ such that the integral

$$P = \int_{x_1}^{x_2} F[x, y(x), y'(x)]\, dx$$

is maximized when two end points (x_1, y_1), (x_2, y_2) are preassigned.

The classical method is to solve the Euler equation

$$\frac{\partial F}{\partial y} - \frac{d}{dx}\left(\frac{\partial F}{\partial y'}\right) = 0$$

for the function y.

For the classical treatment readers are referred to Bliss [2].

*e. **Experimental Search Method.*** There are various experimental designs for the search of extrema, and we shall list a few of them with brief descriptions. For exhaustive treatments readers are referred to Wilde [3]. *Single Variable Search.* Whenever there is only one decision variable, the interval of search for the value of the variable which gives the extremal value to the objective function can be narrowed down by using either the simultaneous method or the sequential. The effectiveness of various methods is expressed by the ratio of initial interval of search I_0 over the interval at nth trial I_n, that is, I_0/I_n. The uniform-pairs method divides the interval equally for search, and the effectiveness is shown as $I_0/I_n = n/2 + 1$. The sequential dichotomous method utilizes past observations in such a way that the interval for search narrows down exponentially according to the number of observations, and its effectiveness is shown as $I_0/I_n = 2^{n/2}$. The most effective search method is probably the Fibonacci search method. It utilizes the Fibonacci series to narrow down the interval and has the effectiveness of $I_0/I_n = F_n$ where F_n is defined as follows:

$$F_0 \equiv F_1 = 1, \qquad F_n = F_{n-1} + F_{n-2} \qquad \text{for} \quad n > 2$$

Kiefer and Johnson developed this search method in the 1950's. It was shown that among all search methods in the single variable search, the Fibonacci method has the minimax property in the sense that the interval by this search is the shortest of all intervals which are the longest possible intervals where the maxima may exist. This was clearly stated by Wilde [3]. The Fibonacci method can narrow down the interval to 1% of the original interval with eleven experiments. There is the golden section method which uses the age-old technique of dividing a section into unequal sections in such a way that the ratio of the whole to the longer section is equal to the ratio of longer section to the shorter section.

Multivariable Search Method. When there are more than two decision variables, it is necessary to use highly sophisticated methods to search the region for extrema. The contour tangent method is a technique that eliminates a region by drawing a tangent line to the contour or response surface and then seeks a point in higher contour area. The tangent line technique is repeatedly applied until the maximum peak is approached. The success of this method presupposes that the response contour is strongly unimodal. The gradient (ascent) method searches a maximum by climbing up a hill to the peak, and it will eventually arrive at the peak (maximum) if the objective function is unimodal. The speed of convergence depends on the scale and technique in finding the steepest way to climb. It does not require that the objective function expressed as response surface be strongly unimodal. However, if the objective function is strongly unimodal, the tangent method can be combined with the steepest ascent method to speed up the search. Recently, Shah, Buehler, and Kempthorne developed the technique of Partan (parallel tangency) which combines the climbing property of ascent method and the elimination property of the contour tangent method, but most of all it utilizes the geometric property of ellipsoidal contours. When two parallel tangent lines touch the ellipsoidal contour, the line which connects two points of tangency passes through the center. This property is easily applied to any ellipsoidal contour, but it can also be used for most of the contours after a few steps of either the ascending or elimination technique are applied.

f.   Linear and Nonlinear Programming.   Whenever an objective function is in linear form with linear constraints on the variables, the maximum (minimum) generally occurs at the boundary so that the differential calculus fails to give the maximum (minimum). The linear programming was developed to circumvent this difficulty. It was started during World War II and was well developed in the postwar period. The method can be simply described as follows. The goal of the linear programming is to find a combination of n variables $(x_1, x_2, \ldots, x_n)$ so as to maximize

$$\sum_{i=1}^{n} a_i x_i$$

subject to the following constraints:

$$\sum_{j=1}^{n} B_{1j} x_j \leqq C_1$$

$$\sum_{j=1}^{n} B_{2j} x_j \leqq C_2$$

$$\vdots \qquad \vdots$$

$$\sum_{j=1}^{n} B_{mj} x_j \leqq C_m$$

The method of solving this problem is called the simplex method. The book by Dorfman, Samuelson, and Solow [4] is recommended to readers interested in an extensive study of this subject. However, linear objective functions are at most crude approximations and very often objective functions are in quadratic or other nonlinear forms. The method for solving cases of nonlinear objective functions with either nonlinear or linear constraints are called nonlinear programming. The difficulty in treating the inequality constraints has yet to be overcome. An advanced treatment of this subject is found in the work of Arrow, Hurwicz, and Uzawa [5].

g. *Dynamic Programming.* The founder and the most important propagator of this method is Bellman [6, 7, 8].

This method is very powerful in treating the optimization of the performance of a process where the whole process can be regarded as a sequence of stages. The number of stages may be numerous, but if decisions at each stage are few, the multistage decision problems can be readily solved by the dynamic programming method with the help of modern computers. A continuous process can be treated in a similar manner by regarding the process as one with a large number of infinitesimal stages. A summary of the technique of dynamic programming is included in Appendix 2. In the field of chemical reactions, an extensive treatment of optimization problems by dynamic programming was done by Aris in both continuous and discrete versions [9, 10].

h. *The Maximum Principle.* The maximum principle was first hypothesized by a Russian mathematician, Pontryagin [11], in 1956. The original Pontryagin's method is confined to continuous processes, that is, processes described by a system of first-order differential equations. They also belong to the category of the simple process. The development of this method is stated in the following section. A summary is also included in Appendix 1.

For a comprehensive study of optimization techniques, readers are referred to Leitmann [12].

2. THE DEVELOPMENT OF THE MAXIMUM PRINCIPLE

Among the numerous attempts to find new mathematical optimization methods, dynamic programming developed by Bellman and the maximum principle derived by Pontryagin are probably the two most successful. The maximum principle was first proposed in 1956 by Pontryagin and his associates [13, 14, 15] for individual types of time-optimizing continuous processes. In the following year, Gamkrelidze [16, 17] proved theorems of the existence and uniqueness and examined the problem of synthesizing time-optimal controls for linear systems. It was fully proved by Boltyanskii [18] in 1958 that the maximum principle was a necessary condition for time optimality.

In 1958, Gamkrelidze [19] extended the maximum principle to a general case in which an arbitrary functional of an integral function is to be maximized or minimized. A detailed presentation of the basic results obtained by Pontryagin and his co-workers can be found in References [11, 20, 21]. A comprehensive treatment of the essential problems in the theory of automatic control, which are associated with the proof and use of the maximum principle, was given by Rozonoer [22].

The first attempt to extend the maximum principle to the optimization of stagewise processes was made by Rozonoer [22] in 1959 for the processes which are linear in the state variables. In 1960, Chang [23] presented the discrete version of the maximum principle for nonlinear, simple processes, which was further explored in his subsequent papers and a book [24, 25, 26]. An algorithm essentially identical to Chang's version, but different in notations, was independently obtained by Katz [27, 28].

Following the procedure used by Katz [27, 28] in the derivation of the discrete version of the maximum principle, we found that the same algorithm can be extended with some modifications to solve optimization problems of a complex process. In the next chapter, we shall derive the discrete maximum principle for optimizing simple feedback processes. The algorithm will be further generalized in Chapter 7 to cover very general classes of complex processes.

REFERENCES

1. Courant, R., *Differential and Integral Calculus*, Interscience, New York, 1936.
2. Bliss, G. A., *Lectures on the Calculus of Variations*, Univ. of Chicago Press, Chicago, 1946.
3. Wilde, D. J., *Optimum Seeking Method*, Prentice-Hall, Englewood Cliffs, New Jersey, 1964.
4. Dorfman, R., P. A. Samuelson, and R. M. Solow, *Linear Programming and Economic Analysis*, McGraw-Hill, New York, 1958.
5. Arrow, K., L. Hurwicz, and H. Uzawa, *Studies in Linear and Non-linear Programming*, Stanford Univ. Press, California, 1958.
6. Bellman, R., *Dynamic Programming*, Princeton Univ. Press, New Jersey, 1957.
7. Bellman, R., *Adaptive Control Processes*, Princeton Univ. Press, New Jersey, 1961.
8. Bellman, R. and S. E. Dreyfus, *Applied Dynamic Programming*, Princeton Univ. Press, New Jersey, 1962.
9. Aris, R., *The Optimal Design of Chemical Reactors. A Study in Dynamic Programming*, Academic Press, New York, 1961.
10. Aris, R., *Discrete Dynamic Programming*, Blaisdell, New York, 1963.

11. Pontryagin, L. S., V. G. Boltyanskii, R. V. Gamkrelidze, and E. F. Mishchenko, *The Mathematical Theory of Optimal Processes* (English Translation by K. N. Trirogoff), Interscience, New York, 1962.
12. Leitmann, G., Ed., *Optimization Techniques with Applications to Aerospace Systems*, Academic Press, New York, 1962.
13. Boltyanskii, V. G., R. V. Gamkrelidze, and L. S. Pontryagin, "On the Theory of Optimum Processes" (in Russian), *Doklady Akad. Nauk SSSR*, **110**, No. 1 (1956).
14. Pontryagin L. S., "Some Mathematical Problems Arising in Connection with the Theory of Optimum Automatic Control System" (in Russian), Session of the Academy of Sciences of the USSR on Scientific Problems of Automating Industry, October 15–20, 1956.
15. Pontryagin, L. S., "Basic Problems of Automatic Regulation and Control" (in Russian), *Izd-vo. Akad. Nauk SSSR* (1957).
16. Gamkrelidze, R. V., "On the Theory of Optimum Processes in Linear Systems" (in Russian), *Doklady Akad. Nauk SSSR*, **116**, No. 1 (1957).
17. Gamkrelidze, R. V., "The Theory of Time-Optimal Processes in Linear Systems" (in Russian), *Izv. Akad. Nauk SSSR, Ser. Matem.* **22**, No. 4 (1958). English translation in Report No. 61-7, Univ. of California, Department of Engineering, Los Angeles, California.
18. Boltyanskii, V. G., "The Maximum Principle in the Theory of Optimum Processes" (in Russian), *Doklady Akad. Nauk SSSR*, **119**, No. 6 (1958).
19. Gamkrelidze, R. V., "On the General Theory of Optimum Processes" (in Russian), *Doklady Akad. Nauk SSSR*, **123**, No. 2 (1958). English translation in *Automation Express*, **1**, 37–39 (1959).
20. Pontryagin, L. S., "Optimal Regulation Processes" (in Russian), *Uspekhi Matem, Nauk*, **14**, No. 1, 85 (1959). English translation in *Am. Math. Soc. Trans.*, Ser. 2, **18**, 321–339 (1961).
21. Pontryagin, L. S., *Proc. of First IFAC Conf.*, Vol. 1, p. 454, Butterworths Publishing, England, 1961.
22. Rozonoer, L. I., "The Maximum Principle of L. S. Pontryagin in Optimal-system Theory," *Automat. Telemech.*, Moscow, **20**, 1320, 1441, 1561 (1960).
23. Chang, S. S. L., "Digitized Maximum Principle," *Proc. IRE*, pp. 2030–2031, December 1960.
24. Chang, S. S. L., "Computer Optimization of Nonlinear Control Systems by Means of Digitized Maximum Principle," a paper presented at IRE International Convention, New York, March 1961.
25. Chang, S. S. L., "Dynamic Programming and Pontryagin's Maximum Principle," *Proceedings of Dynamic Programming Workshop* (Second Annual Pre-JACC Workshop) pp. 109–183, Boulder, Colorado, June 1961.
26. Chang, S. S. L., *Synthesis of Optimum Control Systems*, McGraw-Hill, New York, 1961.
27. Katz, S., "A Discrete Version of Pontryagin's Maximum Principle," *J. Electronics and Control*, **13**, 179 (1962).
28. Katz, S., "Best Operating Points for Staged Systems," *IEC Fundamentals*, **1**, 226 (1962).

3

The Discrete Maximum Principle
for Simple Feedback Processes

In this chapter, we shall derive the discrete maximum principle for simple feedback processes. A generalized algorithm applicable to any type of complex processes will be presented in Chapter 7, where we shall show that the particular algorithm derived in this chapter can be reduced from the generalized algorithm.

1. STATEMENT OF THE ALGORITHM

A schematical representation of the simple feedback process is shown in Fig. 1.2b.* The process consists of N stages connected in series. A portion of the output from the last stage is fed back to the first stage. The state of the process stream denoted by an s-dimensional vector, $x = (x_1, x_2, \ldots, x_s)$, is transformed at each stage according to the decision, denoted by a t-dimensional vector, $\theta = (\theta_1, \theta_2, \ldots, \theta_t)$, made at that stage. The transformation of the process stream at the nth stage is described by a set of performance equations.

$$x_i^n = T_i^n(x_1^{n-1}, x_2^{n-1}, \ldots, x_s^{n-1}; \theta_1^n, \theta_2^n, \ldots, \theta_t^n), \qquad i = 1, 2, \ldots, s$$

or in vector form

$$x^n = T^n(x^{n-1}; \theta^n), \qquad n = 1, 2, \ldots, N \qquad (1)\dagger$$

---

* The first number indicates the chapter.

† The superscript n indicates the stage number. The exponents are written with parentheses or brackets such as $(x^n)^2$ or $[T^n(x^{n-1}; \theta^n)]^2$.

where T^n is called the transformation operator*.

The initial feed enters the system at a rate q, whereas the feedback rate is r. The combination of the feed and the recycle streams is described by the following equation:

$$x_i^0 = M_i(x_1^f, x_2^f, \ldots, x_s^f; x_1^N, x_2^N, \ldots, x_s^N; q; r)$$

or in vector form

$$x^0 = M(x^f; x^N; q; r) \tag{2}$$

where M is called the mixing operator.

When the flow rates, q and r, are constant, equation (2) can be re-written as

$$x^0 = M(x^f; x^N) \tag{3}$$

Since the flow rate is expressed in terms of a conservative quantity, the flow rate entering the first stage is

$$q^0 = q + r \tag{4}$$

A typical optimization problem associated with such a process is to find a sequence of θ^n, $n = 1, 2, \ldots, N$ to maximize, $\sum_{i=1}^{s} c_i x_i^N$, with x^f pre-assigned. Here c_i, $i = 1, 2, \ldots, s$, are some specified constants. The function, $\sum_{i=1}^{s} c_i x_i^N$, which is to be maximized, is the objective function of the process.

The procedure for solving such an optimization problem by the discrete maximum principle is to introduce an s-dimensional covariant vector z^n and a Hamiltonian function H^n satisfying [1]

$$H^n = \sum_{i=1}^{s} z_i^n T_i^n(x^{n-1}; \theta^n), \qquad n = 1, 2, \ldots, N$$

or in vector form

$$H^n = z^n \cdot x^n \tag{5}$$

$$z_i^{n-1} = \frac{\partial H^n}{\partial x_i^{n-1}}, \qquad i = 1, 2, \ldots, s; n = 1, 2, \ldots, N$$

---

* The superscript n attached to the transformation operator T indicates that the performance equations are different from stage to stage, that is, the process is heterogeneous. It is obvious that the derivation of the algorithm for homogeneous processes is obtained by simply removing the superscripts of T in this section. It can be seen that the homogeneous process is, in fact, a special case of the heterogeneous process.

or in vector form

$$z^{n-1} = \frac{\partial H^n}{\partial x^{n-1}}, \qquad n = 1, 2, \ldots, N \tag{6}$$

and

$$z_i{}^N - \sum_{j=1}^{s} z_j{}^0 \frac{\partial M_j(x^f; x^N)}{\partial x_i{}^N} = c_i, \qquad i = 1, 2, \ldots, s \tag{7}$$

and to determine the optimal sequence of the decisions $\overline{\theta^n}$ from the conditions

$$\frac{\partial H^n}{\partial \theta^n} = 0 \quad \text{or} \quad H^n = \text{maximum}, \qquad n = 1, 2, \ldots, N \tag{8}*$$

Both x and z are considered as fixed in maximizing the Hamiltonian.

If the minimizing sequence instead of the maximizing sequence of the decision vector is to be determined, the procedure remains unchanged except that the conditions $H^n = $ maximum are replaced by $H^n = $ minimum.

2. THE DERIVATION OF THE ALGORITHM

In this section, we shall present the derivation of the algorithm stated in the previous section for maximizing the objective function. The algorithm for minimizing the objective function can be derived by simply reversing the direction of inequality signs. The derivation given below is based principally on Katz's original treatment [2] [3].

Let $\overline{x^n}$, $n = 1, 2, \ldots, N$ represent the state resulting from the optimal decisions $\overline{\theta^n}$, $n = 1, 2, \ldots, N$; then

$$\overline{x^n} = T^n(\overline{x^{n-1}}; \overline{\theta^n}), \qquad n = 1, 2, \ldots, N \tag{9}$$

$$\overline{x^0} = M(x^f; \overline{x^N}) \tag{10}$$

If the following independent small perturbations of $\overline{\theta^n}$ are made at each stage,

$$\theta^n = \overline{\theta^n} + \epsilon \phi^n, \qquad n = 1, 2, \ldots, N \tag{11}$$

the disturbances then will alter $\overline{x^n}$ to

$$x^n = \overline{x^n} + \epsilon y^n + 0(\epsilon^2), \qquad n = 1, 2, \ldots, N \tag{12}$$

Here ϵ is a positive parameter which we shall consider to be of the first-order smallness; $0(\epsilon^2)$ denotes both vector and scalar quantities which

---

* It is worth noting that equation (8) is, in general, just a necessary condition for a process in which $T_i{}^n(x^{n-1}; \theta^n)$ are differentiable with respect to the components of θ^n and have continuous first partial derivatives with respect to the components of x^{n-1}. However, for a process whose transformation functions are linear in both x^{n-1} and θ^n, the condition $H^n = $ maximum is not only necessary but also sufficient. A discussion concerning the sufficiency and necessity of the optimal conditions is given in Appendix 4.

represent smallness of a higher order than ϵ; ϕ^n is a t-dimensional vector and y^n is an s-dimensional vector, both being independent of ϵ.

Combining equations (1), (9), and (12) gives

$$\epsilon y^n = T^n(x^{n-1}; \theta^n) - T^n(\overline{x^{n-1}}; \overline{\theta^n}) + 0(\epsilon^2) \tag{13}$$

Expansion of this equation in powers of ϵy yields

$$\epsilon y_i{}^n = \sum_{j=1}^{s} \epsilon y_j{}^{n-1} \frac{\partial T_i{}^n(\overline{x^{n-1}}; \overline{\theta^n})}{\partial x_j{}^{n-1}} + T_i{}^n(\overline{x^{n-1}}; \theta^n) - T_i{}^n(\overline{x^{n-1}}; \overline{\theta^n}) + 0(\epsilon^2),$$

$$i = 1, 2, \ldots, s, \qquad n = 1, 2, \ldots, N \tag{14}$$

Multiplying this equation by $z_i{}^n$ and summing from $n = 1$ to $n = N$ and $i = 1$ to $i = s$ give

$$\epsilon \sum_{i=1}^{s} (y_i{}^N z_i{}^N - y_i{}^0 z_i{}^0)$$

$$= \sum_{n=1}^{N} \sum_{i=1}^{s} z_i{}^n [T_i{}^n(\overline{x^{n-1}}; \theta^n) - T_i{}^n(\overline{x^{n-1}}; \overline{\theta^n})] + 0(\epsilon^2) \tag{15}$$

Combining equations (3), (10), and (12), and expanding the resulting equation in powers of ϵy yield

$$\epsilon y_i{}^0 = \sum_{j=1}^{s} \epsilon y_j{}^N \frac{\partial M_i(x^f; \overline{x^N})}{\partial x_j{}^N} + 0(\epsilon^2), \qquad i = 1, 2, \ldots, s \tag{16}$$

Substituting equations (7) and (16) into equation (15) gives

$$\sum_{i=1}^{s} \epsilon c_i y_i{}^N = \sum_{n=1}^{N} \sum_{i=1}^{s} z_i{}^n [T_i{}^n(\overline{x^{n-1}}; \theta^n) - T_i{}^n(\overline{x^{n-1}}; \overline{\theta^n})] + 0(\epsilon^2) \tag{17}$$

Since $\overline{\theta^n}$, $n = 1, 2, \ldots, N$ is the sequence that maximizes $\sum_{i=1}^{s} c_i x_i{}^N$, the effect of the perturbation represented by equation (11) can only be to make

$$\sum_{i=1}^{s} \epsilon c_i y_i{}^N \leq 0 \tag{18}$$

Combining and expanding the resulting equation in terms of $\epsilon \phi$ give equations (17) and (18)

$$\left\{ \sum_{n=1}^{N} \sum_{j=1}^{t} (\epsilon \phi_j{}^n) \sum_{i=1}^{s} z_i{}^n \frac{\partial T_i{}^n(\overline{x^{n-1}}; \overline{\theta^n})}{\partial \theta_j{}^n} + 0(\epsilon^2) \right\} \leq 0 \tag{19}$$

Since the perturbed decisions θ^n, $n = 1, 2, \ldots, N$ are independent of each other, it may be concluded that each term of equation (19) containing a set of independent variables θ^n must itself be nonpositive. Thus

$$\sum_{j=1}^{t} (\overline{\theta_j{}^n} - \overline{\theta_j{}^n}) \sum_{i=1}^{s} z_i{}^n \frac{\partial T_i{}^n(\overline{x^{n-1}}; \overline{\theta^n})}{\partial \theta_j{}^n} \leq 0, \qquad n = 1, 2, \ldots, N$$

which is equivalent to equation (8). This completes the derivation.

3. THE ALGORITHM FOR THE SIMPLE PROCESSES

The algorithm derived in the previous section can be readily reduced to the form given by Katz [2] for a simple process.

For the process without recycle, the rate of feedback r is equal to zero, and equation (2) reduces to

$$x^0 = x^f \tag{20}$$

and the basic algorithm, equations (5), (6), and (7), becomes

$$H^n = \sum_{i=1}^{s} z_i^n T_i^n(x^{n-1}; \theta^n), \qquad n = 1, 2, \ldots, N \tag{21}$$

$$z^{n-1} = \frac{\partial H^n}{\partial x^{n-1}}, \qquad n = 1, 2, \ldots, N \tag{22}$$

$$z_i^N = c_i, \qquad i = 1, 2, \ldots, s \tag{23}$$

4. EXTENSIONS OF THE ALGORITHM

The algorithm presented in Section 1 can be extended to handle a variety of problems usually encountered in practice. The following examples of the extensions are basically after those made by Katz [2, 3].

a. Processes with Fixed End Points.   For the optimization problem in which some of x_i^N, say x_a^N and x_b^N, are preassigned, and the objective function is specified as $\sum_{\substack{i=1 \\ i \neq a \\ i \neq b}}^{s} c_i x_i^N$, the basic algorithm represented by equations (5) through (8) is still applicable except that equation (7) should be replaced by

$$z_i^N - \sum_{j=1}^{s} z_j^0 \frac{\partial M_j(x^f; x^N)}{\partial x_i^N} = c_i, \qquad \begin{aligned} i &= 1, 2, \ldots, s \\ &\neq a, b \end{aligned} \tag{24}$$

This modification is verified by noting that $y_a^N = y_b^N = 0$, and thus the conditions

$$z_i^N - \sum_{j=1}^{s} z_j^0 \frac{\partial M_j(x^f; x^N)}{\partial x_i^N} = c_i \qquad \text{for } i = a, b$$

included in equation (7) are redundant in obtaining equation (17) from equation (15).

b. Processes with Choice of Initial Values.   Suppose that some of the initial values of the x^f, say x_a^f, x_b^f, and x_c^f are not prescribed, and it is desired to choose these missing initial values as well as the sequence of decisions to maximize x_m^N. The problem may be solved by imposing the following additional conditions:

$$\sum_{i=1}^{s} z_i^{\;0} \frac{\partial M_i(x^f; x^N)}{\partial x_j^{\;f}} = 0 \qquad j = a, b, c \tag{25}$$

to the basic algorithm.

The addition of these conditions is confirmed by observing that when $x_i^f, i = a, b, c$ are not preassigned, equations (10) and (16) must be changed to

$$\overline{x_i^{\;0}} = M_i(\overline{x^f}; \overline{x^N}), \qquad i = 1, 2, \ldots, s \tag{26}$$

and

$$\epsilon y_i^{\;0} = \sum_{j=1}^{s} \epsilon y_j^{\;N} \frac{\partial M_i(\overline{x^f}; \overline{x^N})}{\partial x_j^{\;N}} + \sum_{j=a,b,c} \epsilon y_j^{\;f} \frac{\partial M_i(\overline{x^f}; \overline{x^N})}{\partial x_j^{\;f}} + 0(\epsilon^2) \tag{27}$$

where $\epsilon y_j^{\;f} = x_j^{\;f} - \overline{x_j^{\;f}}$, and $\overline{x^f}$ represents the vector $(\overline{x_a^{\;f}}, \overline{x_b^{\;f}}, \overline{x_c^{\;f}}, x_d^{\;f}, \ldots, x_s^{\;f})$. Accordingly, equation (19) becomes

$$\sum_{n=1}^{N} \sum_{i=1}^{s} z_i^{\;n} [T_i^{\;n}(\overline{x^{n-1}}; \theta^n) - T_i^{\;n}(\overline{x^{n-1}}; \overline{\theta^n})] + \epsilon \sum_{j=a,b,c} y_j^{\;f}$$

$$\cdot \sum_{i=1}^{s} z_i^{\;0} \frac{\partial M_i(\overline{x^f}; \overline{x^N})}{\partial x_j^{\;f}} + 0(\epsilon^2) \leq 0$$

Since $y_j^{\;f}, j = a, b, c$ are independent of each other and of θ^n, it may be concluded that

$$\epsilon y_j^{\;f} \sum_{i=1}^{s} z_i^{\;0} \frac{\partial M_i(\overline{x^f}; \overline{x^N})}{\partial x_j^{\;f}}, \qquad j = a, b, c$$

must all be nonpositive. That is,

$$\overline{x_j^{\;f}} \sum_{i=1}^{s} z_i^{\;0} \frac{\partial M_i(\overline{x^f}; \overline{x^N})}{\partial x_j^{\;f}} \geq x_j^{\;f} \sum_{i=1}^{s} z_i^{\;0} \frac{\partial M_i(\overline{x^f}; \overline{x^N})}{\partial x_j^{\;f}}, \qquad j = a, b, c$$

which are equivalent to equation (25) when there is no constraint imposed on $x_j^{\;f}$.

c.   Processes with Unequal Stages.   It occurs very often that the transformation of state variables at each stage is dependent on the stage number n. For this case, the performance equations are written as

$$x^n = T^n(x^{n-1}; n; \theta^n), \qquad n = 1, 2, \ldots, N \tag{28}$$

Equation (28) can be transformed to the standard form of equation (1) by introducing a new state variable x_{s+1} such as to satisfy

$$x_{s+1}^n = n + 1, \qquad n = 0, 1, 2, \ldots, N \tag{29}$$

Then equation (28) becomes

$$x^n = T^n(x^{n-1}; \theta^n), \qquad n = 1, 2, \ldots, N \tag{30}$$

where $\underline{x}$ represents an $(s + 1)$-dimensional vector $(x_1, x_2, \ldots, x_s, x_{s+1})$. The state variable x_{s+1} satisfies the difference equation

$$x_{s+1}^n = x_{s+1}^{n-1} + 1, \qquad n = 1, 2, \ldots, N \tag{31}$$

Equations (30) and (31) do not have the stage number n explicitly as argument and are of the form of equation (1) with an extra state variable.

From equation (31), it is observed that the initial value of x_{s+1} is

$$x_{s+1}^0 = 1 \tag{32}$$

which is correspondent to the mixing condition for the state variable x_{s+1}. Thus we obtain an enlarged process, which is described by $(s + 1)$ performance equations represented by equations (30) and (31) and $(s + 1)$ mixing conditions represented by equations (3) and (32).

d. Processes with Choice of Extra Parameters. When the performance of a process depends not only on the choice of decision variable but also on an additional parameter σ, our task is to choose a sequence of decision variables θ as well as the parameter σ so as to maximize the objective function of the process.

The performance equations can be written as

$$x^n = T^n(x^{n-1}; \sigma; \theta^n), \qquad n = 1, 2, 3, \ldots, N \tag{33}$$

If a new variable x_{s+1} is introduced such that

$$x_{s+1}^n = \sigma, \qquad n = 0, 1, 2, \ldots, N \tag{34}$$

the system can be described by

$$x^n = T^n(x^{n-1}; x_{s+1}^{n-1}; \theta^n), \qquad n = 1, 2, \ldots, N \tag{35}$$

and the new state variable x_{s+1} satisfies the performance equation

$$x_{s+1}^n = x_{s+1}^{n-1}, \qquad n = 1, 2, \ldots, N \tag{36}$$

Thus the original problem is transformed into one in which we seek a sequence of decision variables and the initial value of the state variable x_{s+1} to maximize the objective function.

e. Processes with Memory in Decisions. If the transformation at a stage is not only a function of the decision variable θ^n but also of θ^{n-1}, that is, the previous decision has effect on subsequent stage, we write

$$x^n = T^n(x^{n-1}; \theta^n; \theta^{n-1}), \qquad n = 1, 2, \ldots, N \tag{37}$$

where the initial decision vector θ^0 is a t-dimensional constant vector k, that is,

$$\theta^0 = k \tag{38}$$

We are to choose the sequence of θ^n to maximize or minimize the objective function of the process.

We introduce a new state vector χ such that

$$\chi^n = \theta^n, \qquad n = 0, 1, 2, \ldots, N \tag{39}$$

and introduce a new decision vector to satisfy

$$\omega^n = \theta^n - \theta^{n-1}, \qquad n = 1, 2, \ldots, N \qquad (40)$$

Substituting equations (39) and (40) into equation (37), we obtain

$$x^n = T^n(x^{n-1}; \chi^{n-1} + \omega^n; \chi^{n-1}), \qquad n = 1, 2, \ldots, N \qquad (41)$$

It is obvious that the new state vector χ satisfies the performance equation

$$\chi^n = \chi^{n-1} + \omega^n, \qquad n = 1, 2, \ldots, N \qquad (42)$$

Equations (41) and (42) are of our general form of equation (1), although the dimension of the state vector is increased to $(s + t)$. Thus we obtain an enlarged process with $(s + t)$ state variables and t decision variables. The $(s + t)$ performance equations at each stage are provided by equations (41) and (42). Equation (38), giving t initial conditions for the t new state variables, is correspondent to the mixing conditions given by equation (3).

f. **Processes with Arbitrary Final Measures as the Objective Function.**
Suppose that we are maximizing $\phi(x^N)$, an arbitrary function of x, rather than x_m^N, a certain component of x^N.

This problem can be reduced to our general algorithm by introducing a new state variable x_{s+1} satisfying

$$x_{s+1}^n = \phi(x^n), \qquad n = 1, 2, \ldots, N \qquad (43)$$

The basic performance equations, equation (1), are then substituted into equation (43) to obtain

$$x_{s+1}^n = \phi[T^n(x^{n-1}; \theta^n)], \qquad n = 1, 2, \ldots, N \qquad (44)$$

which is the performance equation for the state variable x_{s+1}. Instead of the mixing condition, the new state variable x_{s+1} has the following initial condition:

$$x_{s+1}^0 = \phi(x^0) \qquad (45)$$

Thus equations (1), (3), (44), and (45) completely specify an enlarged process with $(s + 1)$ state variables and with x_{s+1}^N as its objective function.

g. **Processes with Cumulated Measures as Objective Functions.** Suppose that in our original process of s state variables $x_1, x_2, \ldots, x_s$, we seek to maximize

$$\sum_{n=1}^N \phi(x^{n-1}; \theta^n)$$

a sum over all the stages of a certain arbitrary function ϕ of the variables

x and θ. An enlarged process with an extra state variable x_{s+1} defined as

$$x_{s+1}^0 = 0 \tag{46}$$

$$x_{s+1}^n = \sum_{n=1}^{n} \phi(x^{n-1}; \theta^n), \qquad n = 1, 2, \ldots, N \tag{47}$$

can be formulated.

It immediately follows that the state variable x_{s+1} satisfies the performance equation

$$x_{s+1}^n = x_{s+1}^{n-1} + \phi(x^{n-1}; \theta^n), \qquad n = 1, 2, \ldots, N \tag{48}$$

The equations (1), (47), and (48), with the initial value $x_{s+1}^0 = 0$, completely specify our enlarged process in $(s + 1)$ variables where the maximization of

$$x_{s+1}^N = \sum_{n=1}^{N} \phi(x^{n-1}; \theta^n)$$

is sought. Equation (46) furnishes an additional condition, which is corresponding to the mixing condition given in equation (3).

In conclusion, the variations of optimization problems can be classified into three general types: (1) variation in the specification of initial or final conditions such as Parts a and b; (2) variation in the form of performance equations such as Parts c through e; and (3) variation in the form of objective function such as Parts f and g. The first type of variation is solved by adding or deleting the initial and final conditions for the corresponding components of z. The second and third types of variation can generally be reduced to the standard form of optimization problem by introducing new state variables or decision variables.

Thus we now see that, although the optimization problem in Section 1.3 appears to be somewhat narrow, it actually can cover a wide variety of problems, if modifications as presented are made.

REFERENCES

1. Fan, L. T. and C. S. Wang, "Optimization of One-dimensional Multistage Processes," *ZAMP*, **15**, 46 (1964).
2. Katz, S., "Best Operating Points for Staged Systems," *Ind. Eng. Chem. Fundamentals*, **1**, 226 (1962).
3. Katz, S., "A Discrete Version of Pontryagin's Maximum Principle," *J. Electron. Contr.* **13**, 179 (1962).

4

One-Dimensional Processes

In this chapter, we shall treat rather extensively a class of multistage decision processes which, for convenience, is designated as a one-dimensional process. Both the simple process and the simple feedback process are considered. The discrete maximum principle developed in the previous chapter for the simple feedback processes is used to derive a recurrence relation of the optimal state and decision for the so-called one-dimensional process. Many practical examples taken from various fields are solved in detail to illustrate the use of such a recurrence relation. At the end of the chapter, we further single out a special class of one-dimensional processes for which the optimal policy is to use the equal value of decision variable at every stage. Such a process is, for convenience, called a linear process.

1. THE PERFORMANCE EQUATIONS

If a multistage decision process can be completely characterized for the purpose of optimization by a single-state variable, the process is called a one-dimensional multistage decision process. A number of multistage optimization problems are associated with this particular class of processes, for example, the optimal solvent allocation for a multistage cross-current extraction process with immiscible solvent [1], the optimal choices of temperature and holding time for a continuous flow stirred tank reactor sequence with a single reaction [2], the optimal design for a multistage process with parallel redundancy [3], and others.

In what follows, we shall first consider the one-dimensional simple feedback process with only one decision variable at each stage. It is obvious that all the relationships derived for the simple feedback process can be reduced to those for the simple process by simply putting the feedback or recycle rate r equal to zero. As we shall see, the result thus obtained can be extended to cover processes with multidimensional decision vectors.

For a one-dimensional process, there is only one state variable x_1 satisfying the performance equation

$$x_1^n = T(x_1^{n-1}; \theta^n), \qquad n = 1, 2, \ldots, N \tag{1}*$$

where T is the transformation operator and θ the decision variable. If q and r are the flow rates of the feed and the feedback streams, respectively, the mixing condition usually can be written in the form

$$x_1^0 = M(x_1^f; x_1^N) = \frac{qx_1^f + rx_1^N}{q + r} = x_1 \quad f \text{ (No REC)} \tag{2}$$

where x_1^f and x_1^N represent the states of the feed and the feedback streams, respectively. In general, the objective function to be maximized is a sum of a certain function of x_1 and θ over all stages of the system such as

$$\sum_{n=1}^{N} G(x_1^{n-1}; \theta^n)$$

The optimization problem associated with such a process is to find a sequence of decision variables θ^n, $n = 1, 2, \ldots, N$ so as to maximize $\sum_{n=1}^{N} G(x_1^{n-1}; \theta^n)$ with x_1^f given.

According to the technique described in Section 3.4, Part g, we introduce a new state variable x_2 satisfying

$$x_2^n = x_2^{n-1} + G(x_1^{n-1}; \theta^n), \qquad x_2^0 = 0, \qquad n = 1, 2, \ldots, N \tag{3}$$

It can be shown that $\sum_{n=1}^{N} G(x_1^{n-1}; \theta^n) = x_2^N$. Thus the problem is transformed into the standard form in which a sequence of θ^n, $n = 1, 2, \ldots, N$ is to be chosen so as to maximize x_2^N for a process described by equations (1), (2), and (3). For convenience, we call x_1 the primary state variable and x_2 the secondary state variable. In general, the secondary state variable has a simple recurrence relationship, for example, it may be linear in itself and hence its introduction will not complicate the problem too much.

---

* The expression in the right-hand side actually should be written as $T_1(x_1^{n-1}; \theta_1^n)$. The subscripts of T and θ are dropped out in equation (1) and the subsequent equations for simplicity.

As we shall see, the complexity of a problem depends mainly on the number of the primary state variables. This is why we call the process with a single primary state variable a one-dimenisonal process.

A number of one-dimensional processes with single control variable has the following form of performance equations

$$x_1{}^n = x_1^{n-1}F_1(\theta^n) + \alpha[F_1(\theta^n) - 1] \tag{4}$$

$$x_2{}^n = x_2^{n-1} + \beta(x_1{}^n - x_1^{n-1}) + F_2(\theta^n), \qquad x_2{}^f = x_2^0 = 0 \tag{5}$$

Here $F_1(\theta^n)$ and $F_2(\theta^n)$ are two arbitrary functions of the decision variable θ^n; α and β are arbitrary constants.

Comparing equations (4) and (5) wtih equations (1) and (3), we immediately see that

$$T(x_1^{n-1}; \theta^n) = x_1^{n-1}F_1(\theta^n) + \alpha[F_1(\theta^n) - 1]$$

$$G(x_1^{n-1}; \theta^n) = \beta[F_1(\theta^n) - 1](x_1^{n-1} + \alpha) + F_2(\theta^n)$$

One of the features of the processes represented by equations (4) and (5) is that the performance equations are linear in state variables. We refer to this particular class of processes as one-dimensional multistage linear processes. It will be shown that the optimal policies for such a class of processes are to apply an equal value of the decision variable at each stage. Any process whose performance equations are not linear in state variables is called a nonlinear process.

2. THE RECURRENCE RELATION OF THE OPTIMAL STATE AND DECISION FOR THE NONLINEAR PROCESSES [4, 5]

In this section a general recurrence relation of the optimal state and decision for the nonlinear one-dimensional processes will be derived. A number of practical examples solved by the recurrence relation will be presented in the next section.

In order to facilitate the presentation, we recapitulate the discrete maximum principle developed in the previous chapter.

To maximize the objective function $\sum_{i=1}^{s} c_i x_i{}^N$, of a multistage decision process described by the performance equations

$$x^n = T^n(x^{n-1}; \theta^n), \qquad n = 1, 2, \ldots, N \tag{6}$$

and the mixing condition

$$x^0 = M(x^f; x^N) \tag{7}$$

where x^f are given and x^N unspecified, the sequence of decision vectors θ^n, $n = 1, 2, \ldots, N$ must be so chosen that the following conditions are satisfied:

$$H^n = \sum_{i=1}^{s} z_i{}^n T_i{}^n(x^{n-1}; \theta^n) = \text{maximum} \quad \text{or} \quad \partial H^n / \partial \theta^n = 0,$$

$$n = 1, 2, \ldots, N \quad (8)$$

where z and x are related by

$$z_\lambda^{n-1} = \frac{\partial H^n}{\partial x_\lambda^{n-1}}, \quad n = 1, 2, \ldots, N \quad (9)$$

and

$$z_i{}^N - \sum_{j=1}^{s} z_j{}^0 \frac{\partial M_j(x^f; x^N)}{\partial x_i{}^N} = c_i, \quad i = 1, 2, \ldots, s \quad (10)$$

For the one-dimensional process, the Hamiltonian function, H^n, can be written as

$$H^n = z_1{}^n T(x_1^{n-1}; \theta^n) + z_2{}^n[x_2^{n-1} + G(x_1^{n-1}; \theta^n)] \quad (11)$$

According to equation (9), the recurrence relations for the covariant variables z_1 and z_2 are found to be

$$z_1^{n-1} = \frac{\partial T(x_1^{n-1}; \theta^n)}{\partial x_1^{n-1}} z_1{}^n + \frac{\partial G(x_1^{n-1}; \theta^n)}{\partial x_1^{n-1}} z_2{}^n \quad (12)$$

$$z_2^{n-1} = z_2{}^n, \quad n = 1, 2, \ldots, N$$

Since the objective function is $S = \sum_{i=1}^{2} c_i x_i{}^N = x_2{}^N$, that is, $c_1 = 0$, $c_2 = 1$, and the mixing condition is

$$M(x_1{}^f; x_1{}^N) = \frac{q x_1{}^f + r x_1{}^N}{q + r}$$

according to equation (10), we write for the process with $x_1{}^N$ unspecified,

$$z_1{}^N = \frac{r}{q + r} z_1{}^0 \quad (13)$$

$$z_2{}^N = 1$$

Substituting equation (13) into equation (12) gives

$$z_2{}^n = 1, \quad n = 1, 2, \ldots, N \quad (14)$$

and

$$z_1^{n-1} = \frac{\partial T(x_1^{n-1}; \theta^n)}{\partial x_1^{n-1}} z_1{}^n + \frac{\partial G(x_1^{n-1}; \theta^n)}{\partial x_1^{n-1}}, \quad n = 1, 2, \ldots, N \quad (15)$$

Hence the Hamiltonian function becomes

$$H^n = z_1{}^n T(x_1^{n-1}; \theta^n) + G(x_1^{n-1}; \theta^n) + x_2^{n-1}, \quad n = 1, 2, \ldots, N$$

According to the second condition in equation (8), θc may be found where

$$\frac{\partial H^n}{\partial \theta^n} = z_1{}^n \frac{\partial T(x_1^{n-1}; \theta^n)}{\partial \theta^n} + \frac{\partial G(x_1^{n-1}; \theta^n)}{\partial \theta^n} = 0$$

Solving this equation for $z_1{}^n$ we obtain

$$z_1{}^n = - \frac{\dfrac{\partial G(x_1^{n-1}; \theta^n)}{\partial \theta^n}}{\dfrac{\partial T(x_1^{n-1}; \theta^n)}{\partial \theta^n}}, \qquad n = 1, 2, \ldots, N \qquad (16)$$

Substitution of equation (16) into equation (15) gives

$$\frac{\dfrac{\partial G(x_1^{n-1}; \theta^n)}{\partial \theta^n}}{\dfrac{\partial T(x_1^{n-1}; \theta^n)}{\partial \theta^n}} = \frac{\dfrac{\partial G(x_1^n; \theta^{n+1})}{\partial \theta^{n+1}}}{\dfrac{\partial T(x_1^n; \theta^{n+1})}{\partial \theta^{n+1}}} \cdot \frac{\partial T(x_1^n; \theta^{n+1})}{\partial x_1{}^n} - \frac{\partial G(x_1^n; \theta^{n+1})}{\partial x_1{}^n}, \quad (17)$$

$$n = 1, 2, \ldots, N - 1$$

and

$$z_1{}^0 = - \frac{\dfrac{\partial G(x_1{}^0; \theta^1)}{\partial \theta^1}}{\dfrac{\partial T(x_1{}^0; \theta^1)}{\partial \theta^1}} \cdot \frac{\partial T(x_1{}^0; \theta^1)}{\partial x_1{}^0} + \frac{\partial G(x_1{}^0; \theta^1)}{\partial x_1{}^0} \qquad (18)$$

Inserting equations (16) and (18) into equation (13) gives

$$- \frac{\dfrac{\partial G(x_1^{N-1}; \theta^N)}{\partial \theta^N}}{\dfrac{\partial T(x_1^{N-1}; \theta^N)}{\partial \theta^N}} = \frac{r}{q+r} \left[\frac{\partial G(x_1{}^0; \theta^1)}{\partial x_1{}^0} - \frac{\partial T(x_1{}^0; \theta^1)}{\partial x_1{}^0} \cdot \frac{\dfrac{\partial G(x_1{}^0; \theta^1)}{\partial \theta^1}}{\dfrac{\partial T(x_1{}^0; \theta^1)}{\partial \theta^1}} \right] \quad (19)$$

Equations (17) through (19) are the recurrence relations of the optimal state and decision. By means of these relationships, a number of optimization problems associated with one-dimensional processes can be readily solved as we shall show in the next section.* Before making studies of

* It may be noted that equation (17) is also applicable to the processes described by equations (1) and (3) in which $x_1{}^N$ instead of $x_2{}^N$ is to be maximized or minimized. Two examples belonging to this class of processes are given in Parts g and h of the next section. A brief derivation of equation (17) for such a process is given as follows.
    From equation (12) we see that $z_2{}^n$ are identical for all n. Let z_2 represent the value of $z_2{}^n$. Dividing the first equation of equation (12) by z_2 and shifting the superscripts from

individual cases, let us briefly outline the general computational procedure involved in using these recurrence relations.

By guessing values for both x_1^{N-1} and θ^N, the corresponding value of x_1^{N} can be computed from equation (1). The result is then inserted into equation (2) to calculate x_1^0. With this calculated value of x_1^0 and the guessed values of x_1^{N-1} and θ^N, we can compute θ^1 from equation (19). Both x_1^0 and θ^1 can also be calculated by iterative applications of equations (1) and (17). The procedure is repeated until the values of x_1^0 and θ^1 computed both ways are sufficiently close.

For a process with no feedback, r vanishes and equation (19) reduces to

$$\frac{\partial G(x_1^{N-1}; \theta^N)}{\partial \theta^N} = 0 \qquad (20)$$

Then, by assuming a value for x_1^N, both x_1^{N-1} and θ^N can be obtained by solving equations (1) and (20) simultaneously, and the corresponding value of x_1^0 can be computed by iterative uses of equations (1) and (17). The whole procedure is repeated until the calculated value of x_1^0 is equal to the given x_1^f. It is worth noting that, for each assigned value of x_1^N, the corresponding values of θ_1^n, $n = 1, 2, \ldots, N$ calculated are the optimal decisions corresponding to the initial condition of x_1^f computed in each run of trial calculations.

To solve a problem with a prescribed end point x_1^N, the first condition in equation (13) or equivalent condition of $z_1^N = 0$ for the process with no feedback is deleted, according to the argument given in Section 3.4, Part a. Consequently, equation (19) or equation (20) for the process with no feedback must also be eliminated. With x_1^N given, θ^N can be computed from equation (1) by assuming a value of x_1^{N-1}. The corresponding value of x_1^0 is obtained by iterative applications of equations (1) and (17), and is then directly compared with the given x_1^f for the process with no feedback. For the feedback process, the computed x_1^0 is inserted into equation

---

$n - 1$ to n, we obtain

$$\frac{z_1^n}{z_2} = \frac{\partial T(x_1^n; \theta^{n+1})}{\partial x_1^n} \frac{z_1^{n+1}}{z_2} + \frac{\partial G(x_1^n; \theta^{n+1})}{\partial x_1^n} \qquad (a)$$

The Hamiltonian function for such a process is given by

$$H^n = z_1^n T(x_1^{n-1}; \theta^n) + z_2[x_2^{n-1} + G(x_1^{n-1}; \theta^n)]$$

Putting $\partial H^n / \partial \theta^n = 0$, we have

$$\frac{z_1^n}{z_2} = -\frac{\dfrac{\partial G(x_1^{n-1}; \theta^n)}{\partial \theta^n}}{\dfrac{\partial T(x_1^{n-1}; \theta^n)}{\partial \theta^n}}$$

Substitution of this expression into equation (a) yields equation (17).

(2) to calculate x_1^f, which is then compared with the given value. The trial calculations are repeated until the computed value is sufficiently close to the given one. Like that of a free end point, the sequence of computed θ_1^n, $n = 1, 2, \ldots, N$ for each assumed value of x_1^{N-1} is the optimal sequence corresponding to the initial condition x_1^f obtained in each run of trial calculations.

When the one-dimensional process has a decision vector of dimension t the performance equations become

$$x_1^n = T(x_1^{n-1}; \theta_1^n, \ldots, \theta_t^n), \qquad n = 1, 2, \ldots, N$$

It can be shown that the following t sets of recurrence relations similar to the set of equations (17) and (19) can be derived for such a process, each set corresponding to each component of the decision vector.

$$\frac{\dfrac{\partial G(x_1^{n-1}; \theta^n)}{\partial \theta_j^n}}{\dfrac{\partial T(x_1^{n-1}; \theta^n)}{\partial \theta_j^n}} = \frac{\dfrac{\partial G(x_1^n; \theta^{n+1})}{\partial \theta_j^{n+1}}}{\dfrac{\partial T(x_1^n; \theta^{n+1})}{\partial \theta_j^{n+1}}} \cdot \frac{\partial T(x_1^n; \theta^{n+1})}{\partial x_1^n} - \frac{\partial G(x_1^n; \theta^{n+1})}{\partial x_1^n}$$

and

$$-\frac{\dfrac{\partial G(x_1^{N-1}; \theta^N)}{\partial \theta_j^N}}{\dfrac{\partial T(x_1^{N-1}; \theta^N)}{\partial \theta_j^N}} = \frac{r}{q+r}\left[\frac{\partial G(x_1^0; \theta^1)}{\partial x_1^0} - \frac{\partial T(x_1^0; \theta^1)}{\partial x_1^0} \cdot \frac{\dfrac{\partial G(x_1^0; \theta^1)}{\partial \theta_j^1}}{\dfrac{\partial T(x_1^0; \theta^1)}{\partial \theta_j^1}}\right],$$

$$j = 1, 2, \ldots, t$$

where $G(x_1^{n-1}; \theta^n)$ and $T(x_1^{n-1}; \theta^n)$ are the shortened forms representing $G(x_1^{n-1}; \theta_1^n, \ldots, \theta_t^n)$ and $T(x_1^{n-1}; \theta_1^n, \ldots, \theta_t^n)$ respectively.

The procedure involved in using these relationships is similar to that described for the use of equations (17) and (19).

3. CASE STUDIES OF NONLINEAR ONE-DIMENSIONAL PROCESSES

A number of optimization problems associated with nonlinear one-dimensional processes is discussed and solved numerically by means of the recurrence relations derived in the previous section. We do not intend to exhaust all possible cases. Our aim is to exhibit that some of the seemingly dissimilar problems, in fact, belong to a same class and thus they can be treated in a unified manner.

a.   Cross-Current Extraction Processes.   The problem of solvent allocation in a stagewise cross-current extraction system without recycle has been solved with dynamic programming by Aris, Rudd, and Amundson [1] and with a nonimbedding technique by Converse [6]. As we shall discuss in Chapter 8, the method of dynamic programming generally requires a large amount of computer memory and very often may introduce a considerable error due to interpolation. Although Converse's nonimbedding technique may reduce the memory requirements and avoid interpolation, its computation time is usually longer than that of dynamic programming and will increase rapidly with the increase in the number of stages in the system.

Rudd and Blum [7] have shown that the dynamic programming tables for the cross-current extraction process without recycle obtained by Aris

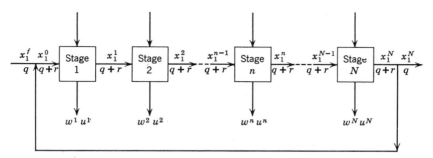

Fig. 1 Cross-current extraction process with recycle.

et al. [1] can be used without modification to determine the optimal operating conditions for the same process with recycle. It was recently pointed out by Jackson [8] that the method is incorrect.

It will be shown here that this process is a one-dimensional process and hence can be solved by means of the recurrence relations presented in the previous section.

A schematic diagram of the process under consideration is presented in Fig. 1. The process consists of N equilibrium stages through which a solvent containing a solute passes. A portion of the end product is fed back to the first stage at a flow rate r. The solute is extracted from the solvent by the addition of wash water at each stage. The solvent and wash water are assumed immiscible. The solvent flows from stage to stage at a rate $q + r$. The state variable is the concentration of solute x_1. The decision variable at each stage is the amount of wash water w. The transformation at the nth stage may be obtained by a material balance for the solute about the stage

$$x_1{}^n = x_1^{n-1} - v^n u^n, \qquad n = 1, 2, \ldots, N \tag{21}$$

Here $v^n = w^n/(q + r)$, and u^n is the concentration of solute in the wash water leaving the nth stage, which is in equilibrium with the raffinate. The mixing of the feed and recycle streams is described by

$$x_1{}^0 = \frac{qx_1{}^f + rx_1{}^N}{q + r} \tag{22}$$

The gross return from the process is the total value of solute extracted. The costs are those associated with the wash water. The net profit is then

$$P = q(x_1{}^f - x_1{}^N) - \lambda \sum_{n=1}^{N} w^n \tag{23}$$

where λ is the relative cost of wash water. The optimization problem is to find a sequence of v^n, $n = 1, 2, \ldots, N$ so as to maximize the net profit with $x_1{}^f$ given. Solving equation (22) for $x_1{}^f$ and substituting the result into equation (23) gives

$$P = (q + r)(x_1{}^0 - x_1{}^N) - \lambda \sum_{n=1}^{N} w^n \tag{24}$$

From equation (21) it is seen that

$$\sum_{n=1}^{N} (x_1^{n-1} - x_1{}^n) = x_1{}^0 - x_1{}^N = \sum_{n=1}^{N} v^n u^n$$

Inserting this into equation (24) gives

$$\frac{P}{q + r} = \sum_{n=1}^{N} v^n(u^n - \lambda) \tag{25}$$

By defining a new state variable $x_2{}^n$ satisfying

$$x_2{}^n = x_2^{n-1} + v^n(u^n - \lambda), \qquad x_2{}^f = x_2{}^0 = 0, \qquad n = 1, 2, \ldots, N \tag{26}$$

it can be shown that $P/(q + r) = x_2{}^N$. Thus the problem is now transformed into one in which $x_2{}^N$ is to be maximized by the   proper choice of v^n, $n = 1, 2, \ldots, N$ for a process described by equations (21), (22), and (26), with $x_1{}^f$ given.

If the phase equilibrium relation is given by

$$u = \phi(x_1) \tag{27}$$

equations (21) and (26) can be rewritten as

$$x_1{}^n = T(x_1^{n-1}; v^n), \qquad n = 1, 2, \ldots, N \tag{28}$$
$$x_2{}^n = x_2^{n-1} + x_1^{n-1} - T(x_1^{n-1}; v^n) - \lambda v^n. \qquad n = 1, 2, \ldots, N \tag{29}$$

Comparing equation (29) with equation (3), it is seen that

$$G(x_1^{n-1}; v^n) = x_1^{n-1} - T(x_1^{n-1}; v^n) - \lambda v^n \tag{30}$$

Differentiating equation (21) with respect to v^n gives

$$\frac{\partial x_1^n}{\partial v^n} = -u^n - v^n \frac{du^n}{dx_1^n} \frac{\partial x_1^n}{\partial v^n} \tag{31}$$

Substituting equations (27) and (28) into equation (31), and then solving for $\partial T(x_1^{n-1}; v^n)/\partial v^n$ give

$$\frac{\partial T(x_1^{n-1}; v^n)}{\partial v^n} = -\frac{\phi(x_1^n)}{1 + v^n[d\phi(x_1^n)/dx_1^n]} \tag{32}$$

Differentiating equation (21) with respect to x_1^{n-1} and then combining with equations (27) and (28) give

$$\frac{\partial T(x_1^{n-1}; v^n)}{\partial x_1^{n-1}} = \frac{1}{1 + v^n[d\phi(x_1^n)/dx_1^n]}$$

The expressions for $\partial G(x_1^{n-1}; v^n)/\partial v^n$ and $\partial G(x_1^{n-1}; v^n)/\partial x_1^{n-1}$ are obtained by differentiating equation (30) with respect to v^n and x_1^{n-1} and then substituting for $\partial T(x_1^{n-1}; v^n)/\partial v^n$ and $\partial T(x_1^{n-1}; v^n)/\partial x_1^{n-1}$ from equations (32) and (33) respectively. The results are

$$\frac{\partial G(x_1^{n-1}; v^n)}{\partial v^n} = \frac{\phi(x_1^n)}{1 + v^n[d\phi(x_1^n)/dx_1^n]} - \lambda \tag{34}$$

$$\frac{\partial G(x_1^{n-1}; v^n)}{\partial x_1^{n-1}} = 1 - \frac{1}{1 + v^n \dfrac{d\phi(x_1^n)}{dx_1^n}} \tag{35}$$

Inserting equations (32) through (35) into equation (17) yields

$$1 + v^n \frac{d\phi(x_1^n)}{dx_1^n} = \frac{\phi(x_1^n)}{\phi(x_1^{n+1})} \tag{36}$$

Solving equation (21) for v^n gives

$$v^n = \frac{x_1^{n-1} - x_1^n}{u^n} = \frac{x_1^{n-1} - x_1^n}{\phi(x_1^n)} \tag{37}$$

Substituting equation (37) into equation (36) and solving for x_1^{n-1} give the following recursion relation:

$$x_1^{n-1} = x_1^n + \frac{\phi(x_1^n)}{\dfrac{d\phi(x_1^n)}{dx_1^n}}\left[\frac{\phi(x_1^n)}{\phi(x_1^{n+1})} - 1\right], \qquad n = 1, 2, \ldots, N - 1 \tag{38}$$

Inserting equations (32) through (35) into equation (19) and then combining with equation (37) yield

$$x_1^{N-1} = x_1^N + \frac{[\phi(x_1^N)]^2}{d\phi(x_1^N)/dx_1^N} \left\{ \left[\frac{1}{\lambda} - \frac{1}{\phi(x_1^N)}\right] - \frac{r}{q+r}\left[\frac{1}{\lambda} - \frac{1}{\phi(x_1^1)}\right] \right\} \quad (39)$$

Thus by equations (38) and (39), the values of state variable x resulting from the optimal policy can be calculated by the trial-and-error method described in the previous section. The computational procedure for this particular case is quite simple, however, for equation (38) does not contain the decision variable. After all the x^n are calculated, the optimal decisions can be readily found by equation (37).

For a three-stage process, equation (39) becomes

$$x_1^2 = x_1^3 + \frac{[\phi(x_1^3)]^2}{d\phi(x_1^3)/dx_1^3} \left\{ \left[\frac{1}{\lambda} - \frac{1}{\phi(x_1^3)}\right] - \frac{r}{q+r}\left[\frac{1}{\lambda} - \frac{1}{\phi(x_1^1)}\right] \right\} \quad (40)$$

Letting n equal one in equation (38) and inserting for x_1^0 from equation (32) give

$$\frac{qx_1^f + rx_1^3}{q+r} = x_1^1 + \frac{\phi(x_1^1)}{d\phi(x_1^1)/dx_1^1}\left[\frac{\phi(x_1^1)}{\phi(x_1^2)} - 1\right] \quad (41)$$

When $n = 2$, equation (38) gives

$$x_1^1 = x_1^2 + \frac{\phi(x_1^2)}{d\phi(x_1^2)/dx_1^2}\left[\frac{\phi(x_1^2)}{\phi(x_1^3)} - 1\right] \quad (42)$$

Now we have three independent relations, equations (40) through (42), and three independent variables, x_1^1, x_1^2, and x_1^3. The simultaneous solutions of these equations will give the optimal values for state variables x_1^1, x_1^2, x_1^3. The value of x_1^0 can be readily calculated from equation (22). The optimal wash water allocation is then determined by equation (37).

Since the process without recycle is a special case of the process with recycle, it is clear that all the equations derived for the latter can be reduced to those for the former by simply setting $r = 0$. Thus equation (22) becomes

$$x_1^0 = x_1^f$$

and equation (39) reduces to

$$x_1^{N-1} = x_1^N + \frac{[\phi(x_1^N)]^2}{d\phi(x_1^N)/dx_1^N}\left[\frac{1}{\lambda} - \frac{1}{\phi(x_1^N)}\right] \quad (43)$$

while the recursion relation, equation (38), remains unaltered. The computational procedure is simplified considerably for the simple process with no feedback. By assigning a value to x_1^N, the value of x_1^{N-1} is computed by equation (43) and the corresponding value of x_1^0 is obtained by iterative uses of equation (38). The trial calculations are repeated until the computed value of x_1^0 is sufficiently close to x_1^f. The optimal values of v^n can be readily recovered from equation (37).

The numerical examples illustrated in Reference's [1] and [7] are recalculated here by means of equations (38) through (43). The phase equilibrium data used are given in Table 1. The results are compared with those of References [1] and [7] in Table 2. For the process without recycle, the slight discrepancy between the results obtained by the two different methods may have arisen from the fact that slightly different equiilbrium data were used in the calculations. It has been mentioned previously that the results obtained by Rudd and Blum [7] for the process with recycle

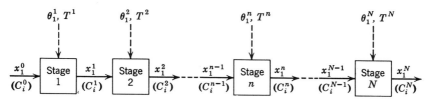

Fig. 2   The continuous-flow stirred tank reactor sequence.

were incorrect, and it can be seen from Table 2 that the profit calculated by the maximum principle is 3.4% higher than that computed by Rudd and Blum.

b.   The Optimal Choice of Temperature and Holding Time with a Single Reaction in a Continuous-Flow Stirred Tank Reactor Sequence. Suppose that a single reaction is carried out in a sequence of continuous-flow stirred tank reactors as shown in Fig. 2.

The equation for a single reaction can be written as

$$\sum_{i=1}^{s} \alpha_i A_i = 0 \tag{44}$$

Here α_i, the stoichiometric coefficient of A_i, is positive if A_i is a product.

If c_i^n is the concentration of A_i in the nth reactor and θ_1^n the holding time, a material balance for A_i about the nth reactor gives

$$c_i^n = c_i^{n-1} + \theta_1^n \frac{dc_i^n}{dt}, \qquad n = 1, 2, \ldots, N \tag{45}$$

If we define the extent of reaction x_1 as

$$x_1 = \frac{c_i - c_{i0}}{\alpha_i} \tag{46}$$

Table 1 Equilibrium Data Used in the Extraction Example

u	x_1
0.000	0.000
0.027	0.010
0.050	0.020
0.073	0.030
0.094	0.040
0.119	0.050
0.138	0.060
0.153	0.070
0.163	0.080
0.170	0.090
0.173	0.100
0.176	0.110
0.178	0.120
0.179	0.130
0.179	0.140
0.180	0.150
0.180	0.160
0.182	0.170
0.186	0.180
0.192	0.190
0.200	0.200

Table 2 Comparison of the Results Obtained by the Maximum Principle and Dynamic Programming for the Extraction Example

	Maximum Principle	Dynamic Programming
(1) Without recycle, $q = 1$, $x_1^f = 0.20$, $\lambda = 0.05$		
Wash Water Allocation		
Stage 1, w_1	0.657	0.647
Stage 2, w_2	0.279	0.284
Stage 3, w_3	0.263	0.260
Profit	0.1071	0.1075
(2) With recycle, $q = 1$, $r = 1$, $x_1^f = 0.20$, $\lambda = 0.05$		
Wash Water Allocation		
Stage 1, w_1	0.5105	0.610
Stage 2, w_2	0.3339	0.440
Stage 3, w_3	0.2977	0.420
Profit	0.1007	0.0974

where c_{i0} is the concentration in a certain fixed reference state, then equation (45) can be rewritten as

$$x_1^n = x_1^{n-1} + \theta_1^n \frac{dx_1^n}{dt}, \qquad n = 1, 2, \ldots, N \qquad (47)$$

When the reaction is carried out under constant pressure, the rate of reaction is a function of temperature θ_2 and concentrations c_i. But it is seen from equation (46) that concentrations are linear functions of the extent of reaction; hence the rate of reaction can be expressed as a function of temperature and the extent of reaction. Thus we may rewrite equation (47) as

$$x_1^n = x_1^{n-1} + \theta_1^n r(x_1^n; \theta_2^n), \qquad n = 1, 2, \ldots, N \qquad (48)$$

The problem is to choose the sequences of temperature θ_2^n, $n = 1$, $2, \ldots, N$, and holding time θ_1^n, $n = 1, 2, \ldots, N$ in such a way that a specified conversion be achieved from a given feed state with the least total holding time, that is, $\sum_{n=1}^{N} \theta_1^n$. According to the technique described in Section 3.4, Part g, we define

$$x_2^n = x_2^{n-1} + \theta_1^n, \qquad n = 1, 2, \ldots, N \qquad (49)$$
$$x_2^0 = 0 \qquad (50)$$

It can be shown that x_2^N is equal to the total holding time, that is, $\sum_{n=1}^{N} \theta_1^n$. The problem is now transformed into that of minimizing x_2^N by the proper choice of θ_1^n and θ_2^n, $n = 1, 2, \ldots, N$ for the process described by equations (48) and (49) with the initial and final conditions

$$x_1^0 = a, \ x_2^0 = 0, \qquad \text{and} \qquad x_1^N = b \qquad (51)$$

It has been known from experience that the optimal temperature policy with a single reaction has a disjoint characteristic, that is, the temperature should always be chosen so that the rate of reaction will be as large as possible at each stage. Here we will show that this characteristic can be deduced from the maximum principle.

Solving equation (48) for x_1^n gives

$$x_1^n = T(x_1^{n-1}; \theta_1^n, \theta_2^n) \qquad (52)$$

The Hamiltonian function for the process is

$$H^n = z_1^n T(x_1^{n-1}; \theta_1^n, \theta_2^n) + z_2^n \cdot (x_2^{n-1} + \theta_1^n)$$

where, according to equation (3.22), the two covariant variables z_1 and z_2

have the following recurrence relations:

$$z_1^{n-1} = z_1^n \frac{\partial T(x_1^{n-1}; \theta_1^n, \theta_2^n)}{\partial x_1^{n-1}}$$

$$z_2^{n-1} = z_2^n$$

The value of z_1^N is unspecified, whereas $z_2^N = 1$.

According to the maximum principle, the optimal choice of the temperature will be found where

$$\frac{\partial H^n}{\partial \theta_2^n} = z_1^n \frac{\partial T(x_1^{n-1}; \theta_1^n, \theta_2^n)}{\partial \theta_2^n} = 0 \tag{53}$$

Differentiating equation (48) with respect to θ_2^n yields

$$\frac{\partial T(x_1^{n-1}; \theta_1^n, \theta_2^n)}{\partial \theta_2^n} = \theta_1^n \frac{\partial r(x_1^n; \theta_2^n)}{\partial \theta_2^n} \tag{54}$$

By combining equation (54) with equation (53) and noting that $\theta_1^n \neq 0$ and $z_1^n \neq 0$, it may be concluded that

$$\frac{\partial r(x_1^n; \theta_2^n)}{\partial \theta_2^n} = 0 \tag{55}$$

This shows that the temperature should be chosen so that the rate of reaction is as large as possible at each stage. Denoting this maximum value by $R(x_1^n)$, we can rewrite equations (48) and (52) as

$$x_1^{n-1} = x_1^n - \theta_1^n R(x_1^n), \qquad n = 1, 2, \ldots, N \tag{56}$$

$$x_1^n = T(x_1^{n-1}; \theta_1^n), \qquad n = 1, 2, \ldots, N \tag{57}$$

Thus the remaining part of this problem is to find a sequence of θ_1^n, $n = 1, 2, \ldots, N$ so as to minimize x_2^N for the process described by equations (49) and (57) with the initial and final conditions given in equation (51). This is again to be solved by using the recurrence relation of the optimal state and decision.

By comparing equation (49) with equation (3), it is seen that

$$G(x_1^{n-1}; \theta_1^n) = \theta_1^n, \qquad n = 1, 2, \ldots, N \tag{58}$$

and therefore that

$$\frac{\partial G(x_1^{n-1}; \theta_1^n)}{\partial \theta_1^n} = 1, \qquad n = 1, 2, \ldots, N \tag{59}$$

$$\frac{\partial G(x_1^{n-1}; \theta_1^n)}{\partial x_1^{n-1}} = 0, \qquad n = 1, 2, \ldots, N \tag{60}$$

It is seen by comparison that equation (56) can be obtained from equation (21) by substituting θ_1^n for v^n and $-R(x_1^n)$ for u^n. Accordingly, both $\partial T(x_1^{n-1}; \theta_1^n)/\partial \theta_1^n$ and $\partial T(x_1^{n-1}; \theta_1^n)/\partial x_1^{n-1}$ can be procured from equations (32) and (33) by the same substitutions; thus

$$\frac{\partial T(x_1^{n-1}; \theta_1^n)}{\partial \theta_1^n} = \frac{R(x_1^n)}{1 - \theta_1^n [dR(x_1^n)/dx_1^n]} \tag{61}$$

and

$$\frac{\partial T(x_1^{n-1}; \theta_1^n)}{\partial x_1^{n-1}} = \frac{1}{1 - \theta_1^n [dR(x_1^n)/dx_1^n]} \tag{62}$$

Inserting equations (59) through (62) into equation (17) yields

$$\frac{1 - \theta_1^n [dR(x_1^n)/dx_1^n]}{R(x_1^n)} = \frac{1}{R(x_1^{n+1})}, \qquad n = 1, 2, \ldots, N-1 \tag{63}$$

Combining equations (56) and (63) gives

$$x_1^{n-1} = x_1^n + \frac{R(x_1^n)\left[\dfrac{R(x_1^n)}{R(x_1^{n+1})} - 1\right]}{dR(x_1^n)/dx_1^n}, \qquad n = 1, 2, \ldots, N-1 \tag{64}$$

As before, the optimal values of x_1^n, $n = 1, 2, \ldots, N$ may be found by the repetitive use of equation (64) together with the initial and final conditions given by equation (51). The optimal holding time for each reactor can be recovered from equation (56).

In what follows we shall consider the cases where the rate of reaction can be expressed as

$$r(x_1; \theta_2) = k_1(\theta_2) \prod_{i=1}^{s} (c_{i0} + \alpha_i x_1)^{\beta_i} - k_2(\theta_2) \prod_{i=1}^{s} (c_{i0} + \alpha_i x_1)^{\gamma_i} \tag{65}$$

where $\beta_1, \ldots, \beta_s$ and $\gamma_1, \ldots, \gamma_s$ are exponents denoting the order of the forward and backward reactions with respect to each species. It will be assumed that $\gamma_i - \beta_i = \alpha_i$, which is true for elementary reactions. k_1 and k_2 are, according to Arrhenius' law, functions of θ_2 only and have the form

$$k_i = k_{i0}\, e^{-Ei/R\theta_2}, \qquad i = 1, 2 \tag{66}$$

Applying equation (55) to equation (65) gives

$$\frac{\partial r(x_1; \theta_2)}{\partial \theta_2} = \frac{1}{R \cdot (\theta_2)^2}$$

$$\times \left[E_1 k_1 \prod_{i=1}^{s} (c_{i0} + \alpha_i x_1)^{\beta_i} - E_2 k_2 \prod_{i=1}^{s} (c_{i0} + \alpha_i x_i)^{\gamma_i} \right] = 0 \tag{67}$$

which can be simplified to

$$\frac{k_1(\theta_{2m})}{k_2(\theta_{2m})} = K(\theta_{2m}) = \frac{E_2}{E_1} \prod_{i=1}^{s} (c_{i0} + \alpha_i x_1)^{\alpha_i} \tag{68}$$

where θ_{2m} represents the temperature which maximizes the rate of reaction for exothermic reaction.†

An explicit expression for θ_{2m} may be obtained by letting $(-\Delta H) = E_2 - E_1$, and substituting equation (66) into equation (68)

$$\theta_{2m} = \frac{(-\Delta H)}{R} \left[\ln \frac{k_{20}E_2}{k_{10}E_1} \prod_{i=1}^{s} (c_{i0} + \alpha_i x_1)^{\alpha_i} \right]^{-1} \tag{69}$$

If there is restriction on the temperature of the form $\theta_{2*} \le \theta \le \theta_2{}^*$, then $\theta_{2m} = \theta_{2*}$ when the value of θ_{2m} given by equation (69) lies below θ_{2*}, and $\theta_{2m} = \theta_2{}^*$ when it lies above $\theta_2{}^*$.

When θ_{2m} lies inside the constraint, substituting equation (69) into equation (65) gives

$$R(x_1) = k_{10} \exp\left[\frac{-E_1}{(-\Delta H)} \ln \frac{k_{20}E_2}{k_{10}E_1} \prod_{i=1}^{s} (c_{i0} + \alpha_i x_1)^{\alpha_i} \right]$$
$$\cdot \prod_{i=1}^{s} (c_{i0} + \alpha_i x_1)^{\beta_i} - k_{20} \exp\left[\frac{-E_2}{(-\Delta H)} \ln \frac{k_{20}E_2}{K_{10}E_1} \prod_{i=1}^{s} (c_{i0} + \alpha_i x_1)^{\alpha_i} \right]$$
$$\cdot \prod_{i=1}^{s} (c_{i0} + \alpha_i x_1)^{\gamma_i} \tag{70}$$

Letting $p = E_1/(-\Delta H)$, equation (70) can be simplified to [9],

$$R(x_1) = k_{10} \left[\frac{k_{20}E_2}{k_{10}E_1} \prod_{i=1}^{s} (c_{i0} + \alpha_i x_1)^{\alpha_i} \right]^{-p} \cdot \prod_{i=1}^{s} (c_{i0} + \alpha_i x_1)^{\beta_i}$$
$$- k_{20} \left[\frac{k_{20}E_2}{k_{10}E_1} \prod_{i=1}^{s} (c_{i0} + \alpha_i x_1)^{\alpha_i} \right]^{-(p+1)} \cdot \prod_{i=1}^{s} (c_{i0} + \alpha_i x_1)^{\gamma_i}$$
$$= \prod_{i=1}^{s} (c_{i0} + \alpha_i x_1)^{\beta_i - p\alpha_i} \frac{(k_{10})^{p+1}}{(k_{20})^p} \left[\left(\frac{E_1}{E_2}\right)^p - \left(\frac{E_1}{E_2}\right)^{p+1} \right]$$

which finally reduces to

$$R(x_1) = \frac{(p)^p}{(p+1)^{p+1}} \frac{(k_{10})^{p+1}}{(k_{20})^p} \prod_{i=1}^{s} (c_{i0} + \alpha_i x_1)^{\beta_i - p\alpha_i} \tag{71}$$

---

† Since the rate of reaction increases monotonously with temperature for reversible endothermic reaction, the temperature that maximizes the rate of endothermic reaction is the highest allowable temperature and therefore is of little interest to us.

For a first-order reversible reaction, $A_1 - A_2 = 0$, with $c_{10}/c_0 = 0$ and $c_{20}/c_0 = 1$, equation (71) becomes

$$R(x_1) = c_0 Q P\left(\frac{x_1}{c_0}\right) \tag{72}$$

where

$$c_0 = c_{10} + c_{20}$$

$$Q = \frac{(p)^p}{(p+1)^{p+1}} \cdot \frac{(k_{10})^{p+1}}{(k_{20})^p}$$

and

$$P\left(\frac{x_1}{c_0}\right) = \left(\frac{x_1}{c_0}\right)^{-p}\left(1 - \frac{x_1}{c_0}\right)^{1+p}$$

Letting $\xi = x_1/c_0$, equation (72) becomes

$$R(x_1) = c_0 Q(\xi)^{-p}(1 - \xi)^{p+1} \tag{73}$$

Substituting equation (73) into equation (64) gives

$$\xi^{n-1} = \xi^n - \frac{\xi^n(1 - \xi^n)}{\xi^n + p}\left[\left(\frac{\xi^{n+1}}{\xi^n}\right)^p\left(\frac{1 - \xi^n}{1 - \xi^{n+1}}\right)^{p+1} - 1\right],$$

$$n = 1, 2, \ldots, N - 1 \tag{74}$$

Thus the optimal values of ξ^n, $n = 1, 2, \ldots, N$ can be calculated by the repetitive use of equation (74). With the calculated values of ξ^n, the optimal holding time can be readily obtained from equation (56), and the optimal temperature from equation (69). The uses of these equations are illustrated in the following numerical example.

Suppose that it is desired to find the optimal temperatures and holding times to increase c_1 from 0 gram mole/cc to 0.8 gram mole/cc in a three-tank reactor sequence for a first-order reversible reaction, $A_1 - A_2 = 0$, with the following kinetic data

$$E_1 = 9.2 \quad \text{kcal/gram mole}$$
$$E_2 = 12.5 \quad \text{kcal/gram mole}$$
$$k_{10} = 10^{5.4} \quad \text{min}^{-1}$$
$$k_{20} = 10^{7.3} \quad \text{min}^{-1}$$
$$c_{20} = 1 \quad \text{gram mole/cc}$$

The values for p and Q are computed from the given data as

$$p = 2.79$$
$$Q = 0.1418 \quad \text{min}^{-1}$$

By the iterative application of equation (74), with a few trial calculations, the optimal values for ξ^n are obtained as

$$\xi^0 = 0$$
$$\xi^1 = 0.5945$$
$$\xi^2 = 0.7365$$

Hence

$$c_1^0 = 0 \quad \text{gram mole/cc}$$
$$c_1^1 = 0.5945 \quad \text{gram mole/cc}$$
$$c_1^2 = 0.7365 \quad \text{gram mole/cc}$$
$$c_1^3 = 0.8 \quad \text{gram mole/cc}$$

Substituting the values of c_0, Q, and p into equation (72) gives

$$R(x_1^n) = \frac{0.1418 \cdot (1 - \xi^n)^{3.79}}{(\xi^n)^{2.79}} \quad \text{gram mole/(cc)(min)}$$

From equation (56), the holding time can be expressed as

$$\theta_1^n = \frac{x_1^n - x_1^{n-1}}{R(x_1^n)}$$

Substituting the appropriate values into this equation for $n = 1, 2, 3$, we obtain

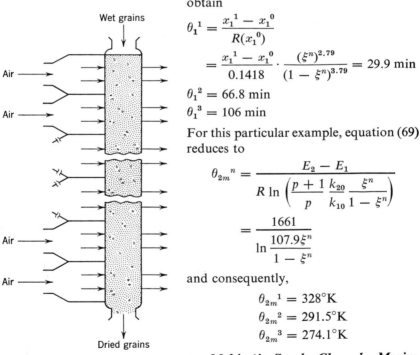

$$\theta_1^1 = \frac{x_1^1 - x_1^0}{R(x_1^0)}$$

$$= \frac{x_1^1 - x_1^0}{0.1418} \cdot \frac{(\xi^n)^{2.79}}{(1 - \xi^n)^{3.79}} = 29.9 \text{ min}$$

$$\theta_1^2 = 66.8 \text{ min}$$
$$\theta_1^3 = 106 \text{ min}$$

For this particular example, equation (69) reduces to

$$\theta_{2m}^n = \frac{E_2 - E_1}{R \ln \left(\dfrac{p+1}{p} \dfrac{k_{20}}{k_{10}} \dfrac{\xi^n}{1 - \xi^n} \right)}$$

$$= \frac{1661}{\ln \dfrac{107.9 \xi^n}{1 - \xi^n}}$$

and consequently,

$$\theta_{2m}^1 = 328°K$$
$$\theta_{2m}^2 = 291.5°K$$
$$\theta_{2m}^3 = 274.1°K$$

Fig. 3 A moving bed grain dryer with N-air supply-channels.

c. Multi-Air-Supply-Channel Moving Bed Grain Dryers [10]. An N-air-supply-channel moving bed grain dryer is diagrammatically shown in Fig. 3 and represented as an N-stage simple process in Fig. 4. Grain, entering the bed from the top and leaving at the bottom, is dried by the air flowing across the bed in N-equally divided channels. x_1^n, $n = 1, 2, \ldots, N$ represent the moisture contents of the grain at the dividing lines of the channels. q represents the total mass flow rates of the grain.

A hot stream of air with humidity h_0 and dry-bulb temperature T_0 enters each stage at the rate of G^n and leaves with an average humidity of h^n. The superscript n stands for the stage number. The material balance with respect to the moisture content at the nth stage can be written as

$$q(x_1^{n-1} - x_1^n) = G^n(h^n - h_0) \qquad (75)$$

or

$$x_1^{n-1} - x_1^n = v^n(h^n - h_0) \qquad (76)$$

where

$$v^n = \frac{G^n}{q} \qquad (77)$$

For concreteness, let us consider the drying of sorghum grain. The decrease of moisture content of the sorghum grain during the drying process is related to the operating conditions by the following set of semi-theoretical equations given by Hukill [11]

$$x_1^n = \left[\frac{(2)^{D^n}}{(2)^{D^n} + (2)^Y - 1}\right](x_1^{n-1} - x_e) + x_e \qquad (78)$$

$$D^n = \frac{\delta \rho \lambda_v(x_1^{n-1} - x_e)C}{qC_pHv^n(T_0 - T_G^{n-1})} \qquad (79)$$

where $Y = \dfrac{t}{H}$

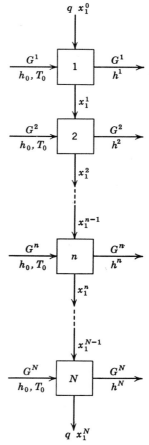

δ = mean distance of grains from the inlet point of air, assumed to be one-half of the bed thickness, ft

ρ = bulk density of sorghum grain, lb/ft^3

λ_v = heat of vaporization of moisture in sorghum grain, Btu/lb

C = the cross-sectional area of air flow channel

H = time required for the moisture ratio, $\dfrac{x - x_e}{x_0 - x_e}$, of fully exposed sorghum to reach a value of 0.5, hr

Fig. 4 A schematic representation of the grain dryer as a stagewise process.

x_e = equilibrium moisture content, percent, lb of water/lb dry solid
C_p = specific heat of air, Btu/(lb)(°F)
T_G = temperature at which the moisture of air is in equilibrium with the moisture of sorghum grain, °F. The curve of T_G versus x_1^{n-1} is given in Fig. 5 [12].
t = time of sorghum grain exposed to drying air, hr
T_0 = dry-bulb temperature of air, °F

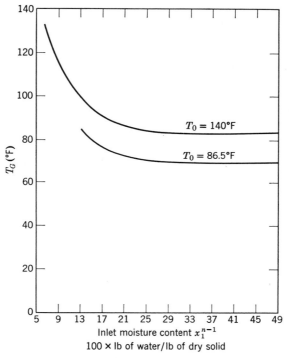

Fig. 5 T_G as a function of inlet moisture content.

In this example, we shall use the following simplified expression for the profit obtained at each stage:

$$P^n = x_1^{n-1} - x_1{}^n - \lambda v^n \tag{80}$$

where λ is the relative cost of hot air.

The problem is to choose the hot air allocation, that is, the sequence of v^n, $n = 1, 2, \ldots, N$ in such a way that the cumulated profit, $\sum_{n=1}^{N} p^n$ is maximum.

According to the technique of Section 3.4, Part g, we introduce a new state variable satisfying

$$x_2{}^n = x_2^{n-1} + x_1^{n-1} - x_1{}^n - \lambda v^n, \qquad x_2{}^0 = 0 \tag{81}$$

It can be shown that $x_2{}^N = \sum_{n=1}^{N} P^n$. Thus the problem becomes that of maximizing $x_2{}^N$ by the proper choice of v^n, $n = 1, 2, \ldots, N$.

If the following substitutions are made,

$$A = \frac{\delta \rho \lambda_v C}{q C_p H} \quad \text{and} \quad d^n = \frac{x_1^{n-1} - x_e}{v^n(T_0 - T_G^{n-1})}$$

equation (78) becomes

$$x_1{}^n = \frac{x_1^{n-1} - x_e}{1 + [(2)^Y - 1]/(2)^{Ad^n}} + x_e \tag{82}$$

Comparing equations (81) and (82) with equations (1) and (3), we obtain

$$T(x_1^{n-1}; \theta^n) = \frac{x_1^{n-1} - x_e}{1 + [(2)^Y - 1]/(2)^{Ad^n}} + x_e \tag{83}$$

$$G(x_1^{n-1}; \theta^n) = x_1^{n-1} - \frac{x_1^{n-1} - x^e}{1 + [(2)^Y - 1]/(2)^{Ad^n}} - x_e - \lambda v^n \tag{84}$$

Partial differentiations of equation (83) with respect to x_1^{n-1} and v^n give

$$\frac{\partial T(x_1^{n-1}; v^n)}{\partial x_1^{n-1}} = \frac{1}{1 + [(2)^Y - 1]/(2)^{Ad^n}}$$

$$+ \frac{(x_1^{n-1} - x_e)[(2)^Y - 1](A \ln 2)}{(2^{Ad^n})v^n(T_0 - T_G^{n-1})\{1 + [(2)^Y - 1]/(2)^{Ad^n}\}^2} \tag{85}$$

$$\frac{\partial T(x_1^{n-1}; v^n)}{\partial v^n} = - \frac{(x_1^{n-1} - x_e)^2(A \ln 2)[(2)^Y - 1]}{(v^n)^2(T_0 - T_G^{n-1})(2)^{Ad^n}\{1 + [(2)^Y - 1]/(2)^{Ad^n}\}^2} \tag{86}$$

Partial differentiations of equation (84) with respect to x_1^{n-1} and v^n give

$$\frac{\partial G(x_1^{n-1}; \theta^n)}{\partial x_1^{n-1}} = 1 - \frac{\partial T(x_1^{n-1}; \theta^n)}{\partial x_1^{n-1}} \tag{87}$$

and

$$\frac{\partial G(x_1^{n-1}; \theta^n)}{\partial v^n} = - \frac{\partial T(x_1^{n-1}; \theta^n)}{\partial x_1^{n-1}} - \lambda \tag{88}$$

Substituting equations (85) through (88) into equations (17) and (20) gives

$$\frac{(x_1^{n-1} - x_e)^2(A \ln 2)[(2)^Y - 1]}{(v^n)^2(T_0 - T_G^{n-1})(2)^{Ad^n}\{1 + [(2)^Y - 1]/(2)^{Ad^n}\}^2}$$

$$= \frac{\dfrac{(x_1^n - x_e)^2(A \ln 2)[(2)^Y - 1]}{(v^{n+1})^2(T_0 - T_G^n)(2)^{Ad^{n+1}}\{1 + [(2)^Y - 1]/(2)^{Ad^{n+1}}\}^2}}{\dfrac{1}{1 + [(2)^Y - 1]/(2)^{Ad^{n+1}}} + \dfrac{(x_1^n - x_e)[(2)^Y - 1](A \ln 2)}{\begin{array}{c}(2)^{Ad^{n+1}}v^{n+1}(T_0 - T_G^n)\\ \times \{1 + [(2)^Y - 1]/(2)^{Ad^{n+1}}\}^2\end{array}}}$$

$$(89)$$

and

$$\lambda = \frac{(x_1^{N-1} - x_e)^2(A \ln 2)[(2)^Y - 1]}{(v^N)^2(T_0 - T_G^{N-1})(2)^{Ad^N}\{1 + [(2)^Y - 1]/(2)^{Ad^N}\}^2} \qquad (90)$$

Thus if we assign a value to x_1^N, the corresponding values of v^N and x_1^{N-1} can be obtained by solving equations (82) and (90) simultaneously. With

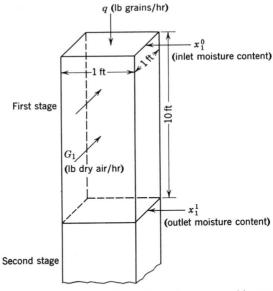

Fig. 6   A section of the dryer showing the dimensions of a stage used in computation.

these values of v^N and x_1^{N-1}, the value of x_1^0 can be obtained by iterative uses of equations (82) and (89). The whole procedure is repeated by trial and error for different assumed values of x_1^N until the calculated value of x_1^0 agrees with the given one. It is, however, worth noting that each run of trial computations yields the optimal policy corresponding to the computed x_1^0. Therefore, all the results from computations may be saved to provide information on the effect of initial value. As an illustration, let us consider the following numerical example.

Table 3 Specifications of Data

Notations	Dimensions	Definitions	Values Used
x_1	$\dfrac{\text{Pounds water}}{\text{Pounds dry grain}}$	Outlet moisture content	Variable
x_1^0	$\dfrac{\text{Pounds water}}{\text{Pounds dry grain}}$	Inlet moisture content	0.21
x_e	$\dfrac{\text{Pounds water}}{\text{Pounds dry grain}}$	Equilibrium moisture content	0.055
t	Hour	Exposing time of the grain to air	0.352
q	lb/(hr)(ft²)	Solid flow rate	1000
ρ	lb/ft³	Bulk density of the grain (sorghum)	35.2
λ_v	Btu/lb water	Heat of vaporization of moisture in grain	1140
C_p	Btu/(lb)(°F)	Specific heat of drying air	0.24
T_0	°F	Temperature of inlet air	140
T_G	°F	See text	Shown in Fig. 5
h_0	lb water/lb dry air	Absolute humidity of inlet air	0.012
Y	Dimensionless	See text	0.352
H	Hour	See text	1.0
δ	Feet	See text	0.5
G	lb dry air/hr	Total mass flow rate of air at each stage	Variable
λ	Dimensionless	Relative cost of air	2.5×10^{-3}

Suppose that it is desired to dry the sorghum grain with an initial moisture content of 21% in a 30-ft high and 1-ft thick bed, as shown in Fig. 6. The grain is supplied from the top at a rate of 1000 lb/hr. Air is supplied at a dry-bulb temperature of 140°F and absolute humidity of 0.012 lb water per lb of dry air. The air-supply-channel is divided into three equal sections each with a height of 10 ft.

The physical properties of air and sorghum grain and other data for this particular illustration are tabulated in Table 3.

By means of equations (82), (89), and (90) and the procedure mentioned, the optimal sequence of v^n was calculated for this illustration using $\lambda = 2.5 \times 10^{-3}$. The results are shown in Table 4.

Table 4   Numerical Results for the Example of a Sorghum Grain Dryer

n	$v^n \times 10^3$	T_G^{n-1}, °F
1	3180	87
2	2940	89
3	2760	92

$$x_1^N = 0.1527$$
$$\text{Profit} \times 10^2/q = 3.51$$

d.   *Simple Heat Exchanger Train.*   Heat exchanger system is one of the most common engineering systems employed in practically every industrial process. Therefore even a minor improvement of its design may result in a substantial saving of cost.

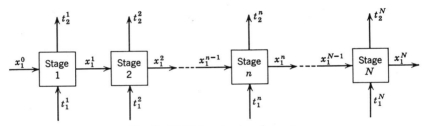

Fig. 7   Multistage heat exchangers.

A heat exchanger system is often operated in a stagewise manner. In this part and the next, we shall consider two different optimization problems associated with multistage heat exchanger systems.

Let us start with a simple heat exchanger train shown in Fig. 7. A cold stream enters the first stage of the train with a certain temperature $x_1^0 = a$, and leaves the last stage with a temperature $x_1^N = b$. At each stage, the cold stream is heated by a hot stream flowing across that stage. The inlet and outlet temperatures of the hot stream at stage n are t_1^n and t_2^n respectively. In what follows we shall restrict our discussion to the case where WC_p, the products of fluid flow rate W and specific heat C_p, are equal for all the streams.

The problem is to select the area θ^n, for each exchanger so as to minimize the total area, with x_1^0, x_1^N, and t_1^n, $n = 1, 2, \ldots, N$ prescribed.

A heat balance at the nth stage gives

$$WC_p(x_1{}^n - x_1^{n-1}) = WC_p(t_1{}^n - t_2{}^n) \tag{91}$$

or

$$t_1{}^n - x_1{}^n = t_2{}^n - x_1^{n-1} \tag{92}$$

which indicates that the temperature differences at the inlet and the outlet are equal. Equating the heat gain of the cold stream at the nth stage to the heat transferred at the same stage, we obtain

$$WC_p(x_1{}^n - x_1^{n-1}) = u^n \theta^n(t_1{}^n - x_1{}^n) \tag{93}$$

where u^n represents the overall heat transfer coefficient at the nth stage.

Solving equation (93) for $x_1{}^n$, we obtain the following performance equation:

$$x_1{}^n = \frac{x_1^{n-1} + U^n t_1{}^n \theta^n}{1 + U^n \theta^n} \tag{94}$$

where

$$U^n = \frac{u^n}{WC_p}$$

By introducing a new state variable x_2, satisfying the following performance equation and initial condition,

$$x_2{}^n = x_2^{n-1} + \theta^n, \qquad x_2{}^0 = 0 \tag{95}$$

the problem is transformed into the standard form in which $x_2{}^N$ is to be minimized by the proper selection of θ^n, $n = 1, 2, \ldots, N$.

Comparing equations (94) and (95) with equations (1) and (3), we obtain

$$T(x_1^{n-1}; \theta^n) = \frac{x_1^{n-1} + U^n t_1{}^n \theta^n}{1 + U^n \theta^n} \tag{96}$$

$$G(x_1^{n-1}; \theta^n) = \theta^n \tag{97}$$

Straightforward differentiations of equations (96) and (97) with respect to x_1^{n-1} and θ^n give

$$\frac{\partial T(x_1^{n-1}; \theta^n)}{\partial x_1^{n-1}} = \frac{1}{1 + U^n \theta^n}, \qquad n = 1, 2, \ldots, N \tag{98}$$

$$\frac{\partial T(x_1^{n-1}; \theta^n)}{\partial \theta^n} = \frac{U^n(t_1{}^n - x_1^{n-1})}{(1 + U^n \theta^n)^2}, \qquad n = 1, 2, \ldots, N \tag{99}$$

$$\frac{\partial G(x_1^{n-1}; \theta^n)}{\partial x_1^{n-1}} = 0, \qquad n = 1, 2, \ldots, N \tag{100}$$

$$\frac{\partial G(x_1^{n-1}; \theta^n)}{\partial \theta^n} = 1, \qquad n = 1, 2, \ldots, N \tag{101}$$

Inserting equations (98) through (101) into equation (17) yields

$$\frac{(1 + U^n\theta^n)^2}{U^n(t_1^n - x_1^{n-1})} = \frac{1 + U^{n+1}\theta^{n+1}}{U^{n+1}(t_1^{n+1} - x_1^n)} \qquad (102)$$

Solving equation (93) for $U^n\theta^n$ and then substituting the resulting expression into equation (102) give

$$x_1^{n-1} = x_1^n + (x_1^n - t_1^n)\left[\frac{U^n(x_1^n - t_1^n)}{U^{n+1}(x_1^{n+1} - t_1^{n+1})} - 1\right],$$

$$n = 1, 2, \ldots, N - 1 \quad (103)$$

Since x_1^N is given, we can start the calculation by assigning a value to x_1^{N-1}. The corresponding values of x_1^n, $n = N - 2, N - 3, \ldots, 2, 1$, can be readily obtained from equation (103). The trial-and-error calculation is continued until the value of x_1^0 computed is sufficiently close to the given one. Then the optimal areas are readily calculated from equation (93).

Table 5 Data and Results for the Example of a Simple Heat Exchanger Train

Data $WC_p = 100,000$		$x_1^0 = 100°F$		$x_1^3 = 500°F$
n		U^n, Btu/(hr)(sq ft)(°F)		t_1^n, °F
1		120		300
2		80		400
3		40		600

Results	θ^n, sq ft		x_1^n, °F	
n	By the maximum principle	By dynamic programming [13]	By the maximum principle	By dynamic programming [13]
1	579	556		
2	1359	1369	182	180
3	5109	5125	295.6	295
Total area	7047	7050		

The simple problem of a three-stage heat exchanger train, numerically solved by Boas [13] with dynamic programming, is recalculated here for illustration. The data used and the results obtained are summarized in Table 5, where the results obtained by Boas [13] are also included for comparison.

e.   A Refrigeration System [14].   In this part, we shall consider a problem similar to the previous one but with more complicated objective function.

Referring to Fig. 7, the hot stream is to be cooled from a certain temperature to a specified lower temperature by N-streams of refrigerant which flow across the stages. The refrigerant enters each stage as a liquid at a given temperature and leaves the stage as a vapor at the same temperature. The overall heat transfer coefficient at each stage is given. The problem is to choose the heat transfer area for each stage so as to minimize the total cost. Furthermore, the assumption made in the previous problem that the products of fluid flow rate and specific heat for all the streams are equal will be deleted in this problem.

Let us introduce the following notations:

$x_1{}^n$ = temperature of tube side material leaving the nth stage
t^n = temperature of shell side material at the nth stage
m = flow rate of tube side material
W^n = flow rate of shell side material

The heat balance around the nth stage heat exchanger in the system will give the following equations.

$$Q^n = U^n \theta^n (\Delta x)_{\ln}{}^n \tag{104}$$

$$Q^n = mC_p(x_1^{n-1} - x_1{}^n) \tag{105}$$

$$Q^n = \lambda^n W^n \tag{106}$$

where

Q^n = the amount of heat exchanged at the nth stage
U^n = the overall coefficient of heat transfer at the nth stage
θ^n = the area of the nth stage heat exchanger
$(\Delta x)_{\ln}{}^n$ = the log-mean temperature difference

$$= \frac{T^{n-1} - T^n}{\ln\left[(T^{n-1} - t^n)/(T^n - t^n)\right]}$$

λ^n = the latent heat of vaporization of the refrigerant.

Combination of equations (104) and (105) gives

$$x_1{}^n = (x_1^{n-1} - t^n)e^{-U^n \theta^n / mC_p} + t^n \tag{107}$$

Combining equations (105) and (106) and substituting equation (107) into the resulting equation, we obtain the amount of refrigerant required at the nth stage, W^n,

$$W^n = \frac{mC_p}{\lambda^n} \cdot [(x_1^{n-1} - t^n)(1 - e^{-U^n \theta^n / mC_p})] \tag{108}$$

The cost of a single heat exchanger is assumed to be a function of the heat transfer area of the exchanger and the amount of refrigerant used and may be given in the following form [15]:

$$P^n = P_c{}^n + P_0{}^n$$

$$= a^n(\theta^n)^{1/2} + b^n W^n \tag{109}$$

where the first term of the right-hand side is the capital cost distributed over the life of the exchanger; the second term is the operating cost; a^n and b^n are constants at the nth stage. It may be noted that the amount of refrigerant required at the nth stage W^n is a function of the exchanger area as shown in equation (108).

The problem is to choose the sequence of θ^n, $n = 1, 2, \ldots, N$ so as to minimize the total cost, $\sum_{n=1}^{N} P^n$, with $x_1{}^0$, $x_1{}^N$, m, and t^n, $n = 1, 2, \ldots, N$ preassigned.

Again, we employ the technique presented in Section 3.4, Part g, to reduce the problem to the standard form.

A new state variable x_2 is introduced to satisfy

$$x_2{}^n = x_2^{n-1} + P^n, \qquad n = 1, 2, \ldots, N \tag{110}$$

$$x_2{}^0 = 0 \tag{111}$$

Then the problem becomes that of minimizing $x_2{}^N$ by the proper choice of θ^n, $n = 1, 2, \ldots, N$ for a process described by equations (107), (110), and (111), with the following boundary conditions

$$x_1{}^0 = T^0$$
$$x_1{}^N = T^N \tag{112}$$

Substituting equation (109) into equation (110) and inserting equation (108) into the resulting equation, we obtain

$$x_2{}^n = x_2^{n-1} + a^n(\theta^n)^{1/2} + \frac{b^n m C_p}{\lambda^n} [(x_1^{n-1} - t^n)(1 - e^{-U^n\theta^n/mC_p})],$$

$$n = 1, 2, \ldots, N \tag{113}$$

Comparing equations (107) and (113) with equations (1) and (3), we obtain

$$T(x_1^{n-1}; \theta^n) = (x_1^{n-1} - t^n)e^{-U^n\theta^n/mC_p} + t^n \tag{114}$$

and

$$G(x_1^{n-1}; \theta^n) = a^n(\theta^n)^{1/2} + \frac{b^n m C_p}{\lambda^n} [(x_1^{n-1} - t^n)(1 - e^{-U^n\theta^n/mC_p})] \tag{115}$$

Partial differentiations of equations (114) and (115) with respect to x_1^{n-1} and θ^n yield

$$\frac{\partial T(x_1^{n-1}; \theta^n)}{\partial x_1^{n-1}} = e^{-U^n \theta^n / m C_p} \tag{116}$$

$$\frac{\partial T(x_1^{n-1}; \theta^n)}{\partial \theta^n} = -\frac{(x_1^{n-1} - t^n) U^n}{m C_p} e^{-U^n \theta^n / m C_p} \tag{117}$$

$$\frac{\partial G(x_1^{n-1}; \theta^n)}{\partial x_1^{n-1}} = \frac{b^n m C_p}{x^n} (1 - e^{-U^n \theta^n / m C_p}) \tag{118}$$

$$\frac{\partial G(x_1^{n-1}; \theta^n)}{\partial \theta^n} = \frac{a^n}{2(\theta^n)^{1/2}} + \frac{b^n U^n}{\lambda^n} (x_1^{n-1} - t^n) e^{-U^n \theta^n / m C_p} \tag{119}$$

Substituting these expressions into equation (17) gives

$$\frac{b^n m C_p}{\lambda^n} + \frac{a^n e^{U^n \theta^n / m C_p}}{2(\theta^n)^{1/2}(x_1^{n-1} - t^n)(U^n / m C_p)} = \frac{a^{n+1}}{2(\theta^{n+1})^{1/2}(x_1^n - t^{n+1})(U^{n+1} / m C_p)}$$
$$+ \frac{b^{n+1} m C_p}{\lambda^{n+1}}, \qquad n = 1, 2, \ldots, N \tag{120}$$

Since all the parameters b^n, λ^n, a^n, U^n, and t^n, $n = 1, 2, \ldots, N$ are given, it is obvious that θ^{n+1} can be calculated from equation (120) if x_1^{n-1}, x_1^n, and θ^n are known.

If we let

$$f(x_1^{n-1}; \theta^n) = \frac{a^n e^{U^n \theta^n / m C_p}}{2(\theta^n)^{1/2}(x_1^{n-1} - t^n)(U^n / m C_p)} + \frac{b^n m C_p}{\lambda^n} \tag{121}$$

then solving equation (120) for θ^{n+1} gives

$$\theta^{n+1} = \left\{ \frac{a^{n+1}}{[f(x_1^{n-1}; \theta^n) - b^{n+1} m C_p / \lambda^{n+1}] 2(x_1^n - t^{n+1})(U^{n+1} / m C_p)} \right\}^2,$$
$$n = 1, 2, \ldots, N \tag{122}$$

The computation for this problem can be carried out as follows:

Step 1. Assume a value for θ^1.

Step 2. Since $x_1^0 (= T^0)$ is given, x_1^1 can be calculated from equation (107).

Step 3. Calculate θ^2 from equation (122).

Step 4. Repeat steps 2 and 3 for every stage.

Step 5. If x_1^N calculated is equal to T^N, the sequence of θ^n thus obtained is the optimal policy, that is, the sequence of the heat transfer areas which will give the minimum cost of the system.

Step 6. If x_1^N calculated is not equal to T^N given, a new value for θ^1 is assumed and steps 1 to 5 are repeated.

Table 6   Data Used for the Three-Stage Heat Exchanger (See Fig. 7)

Symbol	Item	Unit	Stage 1	Stage 2	Stage 3
t^n	Temperature of refrigerant	°F	0	−40	−80
λ^n	Latent heat of the refrigerant	$\dfrac{\text{Btu}}{\text{lb}}$	100	100	100
U^n	The overall heat transfer coefficient	Btu/ (hr)(ft²)(°F)	200	200	200
a^n	Constant for the capital cost	$/(hr)(ft²)^{1/2}$	0.05	0.05	0.05
b^n	Constant for the operating cost	$/lb	2×10^{-4}	3×10^{-4}	4×10^{-4}

$$T^0 = 50°F, \; T^N = -70°F$$

$$m = 10{,}000 \text{ lb/hr}$$

$$C_p = 1.0 \, \frac{\text{Btu}}{\text{lb °F}}$$

It is worthwhile to note that for each assumed value of θ^1, the corresponding value of θ^n, $n = 2, 3, \ldots, N$ computed are the optimal control actions corresponding to the given initial condition $x_1^0 \, (= T^0)$ and the final condition x_1^N obtained in each run of trial calculations.

The computational procedure mentioned above is programmed for numerical solution of a three-stage process on an IBM 1620 computer.

The data used in the computation are shown in Table 6. The values selected are simply for the purpose of illustration.

Table 7   Optimal Design for a Three-Stage Heat Exchanger with $T^0 \, (= x_1^0) = 50°F$ and $T^N \, (= x_1^3) = -70°F$

Symbol	Item	Unit	Stage 1	Stage 2	Stage 3
x_1^{n-1}	Inlet temperature of the stage	°F	50	11.34	−28.67
x_1^n	Outlet temperature of the stage	°F	11.34	−28.67	−70.00
θ^n	Heat transfer area	ft²	74.206	75.543	81.788
W^n	Amount of refrigerant	lb/hr	3866.5	4000.4	4133.1
x_2^n	Total cost by the stage	$/hr	1.2040	2.8387	4.9441

Table 7 shows the results of the calculation. It has been mentioned that for each trial calculation, corresponding to the assumed θ^1, a sequence of θ^n, $n = 2, 3$ and the corresponding values of x_1^3 are obtained. Such a sequence of θ^n, $n = 1, 2, 3$ is the optimal policy corresponding to the given $x_1^0 (= T^0)$ and the calculated x_1^3. Table 8 shows some of the results of the trial calculations.

Table 8 Optimal Design for Three-Stage Heat Exchanger (with Different Outlet Temperatures)

1. Optimal Design for $T^0 (= x_1^0) = 50°F$ and $T^N (= x_1^3) = -47.25°$

Symbol	Item	Unit	Stage 1	Stage 2	Stage 3
x_1^{n-1}	Same as in Table 7	°F	50	11.73	-31.81
x_1^n		°F	11.73	-31.81	-47.25
θ^n		ft^2	72.50	92.176	19.306
W^n		lb/hr	3827.1	4354.2	1543.5
x_2^n		$/hr	1.1912	2.9775	3.8146

2. Optimal Design for $T^0 (= x_1^0) = 50°F$ and $T^N (= x_1^3) = -66.78°F$

x_1^{n-1}	Same as in Table 7	°F	50	11.38	-29.05
x_1^n		°F	11.38	-29.05	-66.78
θ^n		ft^2	74.00	77.31	67.46
W^n		lb/hr	3861.8	4043.6	3772.9
x_2^n		$/hr	1.2025	2.8552	4.7750

3. Optimal Design for $T^0 = 50°F$ and $T^N = -74.18°F$

x_1^{n-1}	Same as in Table 7	°F	50	11.27	-28.12
x_1^n		°F	11.27	-28.12	-74.18
θ^n		ft^2	74.50	73.10	109.4
W^n		lb/hr	3873.1	3938.6	4606.4
x_2^n		$/hr	1.2062	2.8153	5.1808

4. Optimal Design for $T^0 = 50°F$ and $T^N = -78.79°F$

x_1^{n-1}	Same as in Table 7	°F	50	11.16	-27.18
x_1^n		°F	11.16	-27.18	-78.79
θ^n		ft^2	75.00	69.99	189.0
W^n		lb/hr	3884.3	3833.6	5161.5
x_2^n		$/hr	1.2099	2.7759	5.5279

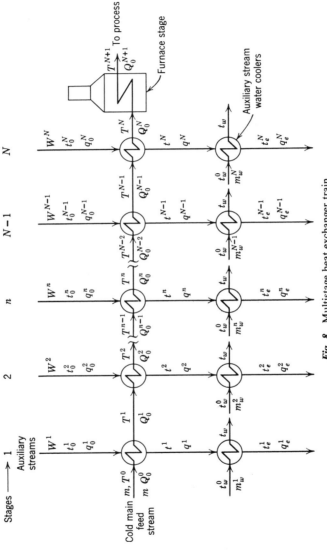

Fig. 8 Multistage heat exchanger train.

We conclude our treatment of the heat exchanger by mentioning that a complicated multistage heat exchanger train such as shown in Fig. 8 [15] can also be dealt with in the same way. In this system a cold main stream is to be heated up to a certain temperature by a furnace and hot auxiliary streams, which are in turn to be cooled from a given temperature to a certain temperature. The problem is to find the optimal heat allocation policy to minimize the total costs of the system.

f. *The Adiabatic Tubular Reactors Sequence* [16]. In an exothermic reversible reaction, the equilibrium conversion decreases exponentially, and the specific reaction rate increases exponentially as the temperature

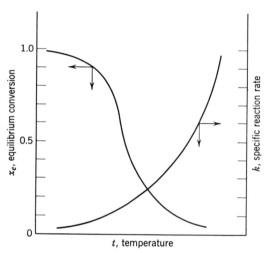

Fig. 9 Effect of temperature on equilibrium conversion and specific reaction rate.

increases, as shown in Fig. 9. It can be seen that, although a high reaction rate can be obtained at a high temperature, the conversion is limited to a very low value; and that although a high conversion can be obtained at a low temperature, the reaction rate is very slow. Both extreme cases are undesirable. Hence it is usually suggested that such a reaction be carried out in several stages connected in series as shown in Fig. 10, using high temperature for the earlier stages to obtain a high reaction rate at the beginning of the reaction and using low temperature for the later stages to achieve a high conversion at the end of the reaction [17]. For an exothermic reaction, if each stage is assumed to be adiabatic, the outlet temperature from each stage would be higher than the inlet temperature. Usually cooling of the reactant to an optimal temperature is desirable before entering each stage. The problem then is to determine the optimal number of stages and the optimal sequences of the inlet temperature and the outlet conversion for each stage so that a specified final conversion can be accomplished with a minimum amount of catalyst or a minimum total volume of the reactor. In Chapter 6, we shall consider a more complicated case of maximizing the profit for such a sequence of adiabatic tubular reactors.

The design equation of a catalytic plug flow reactor is

$$F \, dx = r \, dw \tag{123}$$

where F is the mass flow rate of the reaction mixture passing through the

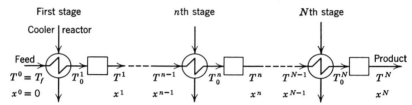

Fig. 10   A multistage adiabatic reactor scheme.

reactor; x is the conversion; w is the catalyst weight; and r is the reaction rate defined as the formation of the product per unit time per unit weight of the catalyst. The reaction rate r is assumed to be a function of the conversion x and the reaction temperature T; that is,

$$r = f(x, T) \tag{124}$$

For an adiabatic reactor, the energy balance equation is

$$C_p(T - T_0) = \Delta H \cdot x \tag{125}$$

where C_p is the average heat capacity of the reaction mixture; T_0 is the temperature at the inlet of the reactor; and ΔH is the heat of reaction.

By substituting equation (125) into equation (124), the reaction rate r can be expressed as a function of the inlet temperature T_0 and the conversion x; that is,

$$r = r(T_0, x) \tag{126}$$

Substituting equation (126) into equation (123) yields

$$F \, dx = r(T_0, x) \, dw$$

or after integrating

$$\frac{w}{F} = \int_0^x \frac{dx}{r(T_0, x)} \tag{127}$$

In order to apply the discrete maximum principle, the sequence of reactors is represented as a multistage process shown in Fig. 11. The two state variables are

x_1: conversion

x_2: sum of the catalyst weights from the first stage to the nth stage inclusive; that is, $\sum_{n=1}^{n} w^n$

and the two decision variables are

θ_1: inlet temperature of each stage

θ_2: catalyst weight of each stage

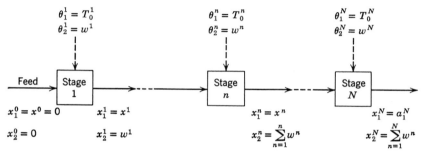

Fig. 11 A simplified multistage adiabatic reactor scheme.

With these notations, equation (126) may be rewritten as

$$\frac{\theta_2{}^n}{F} = \int_{x_1{}^{n-1}}^{x_1{}^n} \frac{dx_1}{r(\theta_1{}^n, x_1)}, \qquad n = 1, 2, \ldots, N \qquad (128)$$

which indicates that $x_1{}^n$ is a function of x_1^{n-1}, $\theta_1{}^n$, and $\theta_2{}^n$. Thus we may write

$$x_1{}^n = T(x_1^{n-1}; \theta_1{}^n, \theta_2{}^n)$$

From the definition of x_2, we have

$$x_2{}^n = x_2^{n-1} + \theta_2{}^n, \qquad n = 1, 2, \ldots, N \qquad (129)$$

and

$$x_2{}^0 = 0 \qquad (130)$$

Since there is no conversion before entering the reactor

$$x_1{}^0 = 0 \qquad (131)$$

The final conversion is given as

$$x_1{}^N = a_1{}^N \qquad (132)$$

The problem now is formulated as that of finding the sequences of θ_1^n and θ_2^n to minimize x_2^N for a process described by equations (128) to (132).

When we regard x_1^n as the only dependent variable and partially differentiate equation (128) with respect to x_1^{n-1}, θ_1^n, and θ_2^n, we obtain

$$\frac{\partial T(x_1^{n-1}; \theta_1^n, \theta_2^n)}{\partial x_1^{n-1}} = \frac{\partial x_1^n}{\partial x_1^{n-1}} = \frac{r(\theta_1^n, x_1^n)}{r(\theta_1^n, x_1^{n-1})}, \qquad n = 1, 2, \ldots, N \quad (133)$$

$$\frac{\partial T(x_1^{n-1}; \theta_1^n, \theta_2^n)}{\partial \theta_1^n} = \frac{\partial x_1^n}{\partial \theta_1^n} = -r(\theta_1^n, x_1^n) \int_{x_1^{n-1}}^{x_1^n} \frac{\partial}{\partial \theta_1^n}\left(\frac{1}{r(\theta_1^n, x_1)}\right) dx_1,$$
$$n = 1, 2, \ldots, N \quad (134)$$

$$\frac{\partial T(x_1^{n-1}; \theta_1^n, \theta_2^n)}{\partial \theta_2^n} = \frac{\partial x_1^n}{\partial \theta_2^n} = \frac{r(\theta_1^n, x_1^n)}{F}, \qquad n = 1, 2, \ldots, N \quad (135)$$

Comparing equation (129) with equation (3), we obtain

$$G(x_1^{n-1}; \theta_1^n, \theta_2^n) = \theta_2^n$$

It follows that

$$\frac{\partial G(x_1^{n-1}; \theta_1^n, \theta_2^n)}{\partial x_1^{n-1}} = 0, \qquad n = 1, 2, \ldots, N \quad (136)$$

$$\frac{\partial G(x_1^{n-1}; \theta_1^n, \theta_2^n)}{\partial \theta_2^n} = 1, \qquad n = 1, 2, \ldots, N \quad (137)$$

Substitutions of equations (133), (135), (136), and (137) into equation (17) give

$$r(\theta_1^n, x_1^n) = r(\theta_1^{n+1}, x_1^n), \qquad n = 1, 2, \ldots, N-1 \quad (138)$$

This gives one of the optimality conditions for the multistage process under consideration. This condition indicates that the reaction rate at the outlet of each stage is equal to that at the inlet of the following stage.

Another optimality condition can be found as follows.

The Hamiltonian function for the process is

$$H^n = z_1^n x_1^n + x_2^{n-1} + \theta_2^n, \qquad n = 1, 2, \ldots, N \quad (139)$$

According to the maximum principle, we put

$$\frac{\partial H^n}{\partial \theta_1^n} = z_1^n \frac{\partial x_1^n}{\partial \theta_1^n} = 0 \quad (140)$$

It follows

$$\frac{\partial x_1^n}{\partial \theta_1^n} = 0, \qquad n = 1, 2, \ldots, N \quad (141)$$

Substituting equation (134) into equation (141) gives

$$\int_{x_1^{n-1}}^{x_1^{n}} \frac{\partial}{\partial \theta_1^{n}} \left[\frac{1}{r(\theta_1^{n}, x_1)} \right] dx_1 = 0, \qquad n = 1, 2, \ldots, N \qquad (142)$$

This is another optimality condition.

Thus the optimization problem can be solved by the following procedure, utilizing the two optimality conditions, equations (138) and (142), together with the performance equations (128) and (129).

Step 1.   Choose a value for N.

Step 2.   Assume a value for θ_1^1.

Step 3.   Calculate x_1^1 from equation (142).

Step 4.   With these values of x_1^1 and θ_1^1, calculate θ_1^2 from equation (138).

Step 5.   Repeat steps 3 and 4 to obtain all the values of x_1^n and θ_1^n, $n = 3, 4, \ldots, N$.

Step 6.   If x_1^N so obtained is equal to a_1^N, the problem is solved. If $x_1^N \neq a_1^N$, assume another value for θ_1^1 and repeat from step 3 until $x_1^N = a_1^N$.

Step 7.   Substitute the values of x_1^n and θ_1^n into equation (128) to calculate θ_2^n.

Step 8.   Substitute equation (130) and the values of θ_2^n into equation (129) to calculate x_2^n. x_2^N will be the minimum amount of the catalyst required for the chosen number of stages N.

Step 9.   Repeat for several values of N to find the optimal one which gives the smallest value of x_2^N.

The optimal conditions given in equations (138) and (142) are identical to those obtained by Konoki [18] with the use of the method of differential calculus. Using a graphical method which is equivalent to the numerical method described, Konoki solved a three-stage optimization problem of the water gas reaction process. He noted that if such a problem is to be solved by dynamic programming, the required computational time is 120-folds of that required by his method [19].

*g.   **Step Rockets** I* [20].   In this and the next parts, the optimization problems associated with step rockets are discussed. A step rocket is a multistage rocket system employing the technique of jettisoning structural weight during flight to improve the performance. An N-step rocket is diagrammatically shown in Fig. 12 and represented as a multistage process in Fig. 13. A stage refers to the period of time from the instance just after the jettison of one structural package to the instance just after the jettison or cutoff of the next one.

The optimization problem associated with such a step rocket is to find the optimal weight distribution among different stages to maximize or minimize a certain objective function.

The problem treated here assumes that the structure ratio and the exhaust speed are constants for each stage. In the next part, we shall

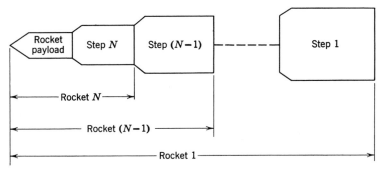

Fig. 12   A sketch of an N-step rocket.

consider the case for which the structure ratio is a function of stage weight. Both these two parts use the growth factor as the objective function, which is to be minimized. In Chapter 6, the problem of minimizing the hardware weight will be investigated.

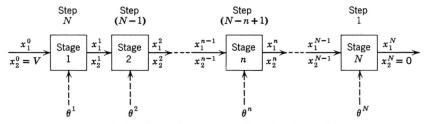

Fig. 13   Stagewise representation of a step rocket.

In what follows we shall consider an N-stage rocket vehicle moving linearly in zero-gravity field with preassigned values of (1) total ideal speed V, (2) weight of payload, (3) exhaust speed of nth stage C^n, and (4) structure ratio of nth stage ϵ^n.

Let us first introduce the following notations.

Burnout ratio or mass ratio of the nth stage

$$r^n = \frac{W_0{}^n}{W_c{}^n} = \frac{\text{weight of vehicle at ignition of the } n\text{th stage}}{\text{weight of vehicle at cutoff of the } n\text{th stage}}$$

Payload ratio of the nth stage

$$\lambda^n = \frac{\text{weight of vehicle at ignition of the } n\text{th stage}}{\substack{\text{weight of payload of the } n\text{th stage, that is, weight of vehicle} \\ \text{at ignition of the } (n-1)\text{th stage}}}$$

$$= \frac{W_0{}^n}{W_0^{n-1}}$$

Structure ratio of the nth stage

$$\epsilon^n = \frac{W_s{}^n}{W_0{}^n} = \frac{\substack{\text{weight of vehicle at cutoff of the } n\text{th stage minus weight} \\ \text{of payload of the } n\text{th stage}}}{\text{weight of vehicle at ignition of the } n\text{th stage}}$$

The performance capability of a multistage rocket vehicle can be described by two equations, one representing the growth factor G and the other the cutoff speed V_c.

$$G = \frac{\text{launching weight}}{\text{payload weight}} = \frac{W_0{}^N}{W_0{}^0} = \prod_{n=1}^{N} \lambda^n \qquad (143)$$

$$V_c = \sum_{n=1}^{N} C^n \ln r^n - \delta V \qquad (144)$$

where

$$r^n = \frac{\lambda^n}{1 + \epsilon^n \lambda^n} \qquad (145)$$

δV in equation (144) is the speed loss associated with gravity and drag. When $\delta V = 0$, equation (144) becomes

$$V = \sum_{n=1}^{N} C^n \ln r^n \qquad (146)$$

where V is called total ideal speed.

In this problem, the structure ratios ϵ^n, and the exhaust speed of propellant C^n, are considered to be constant at each stage, although they may be different in values from stage to stage.

The problem can be considered as one of finding the optimum weight distribution in order to (1) minimize the growth factor G with the total ideal speed V given or (2) maximize the total ideal speed V with the growth factor G given.

Each of the following quantities can be used as the decision variable: (1) the payload ratio of each stage λ^n, (2) the burnout ratio r^n, (3) the weight of each stage $(W_0{}^n - W_0^{n-1})$, or (4) the propellant parameter $[(W_0{}^n - W_c{}^n)/W_0{}^n = 1 - 1/r^n]$.

The same problem has been examined by many investigators with different decision variables and methods. Regarding the payload ratio as the decision variable, Hall and Zambelli [21] solved the problem by the technique of Lagrangian multiplier. Ragsac and Patterson [22] improved the solution by giving an upper bound on the Lagrangian multiplier which facilitates the iteration procedure.

Here we shall show how the problem can be treated by the discrete maximum principle.

Let us consider at first the problem of minimizing the growth factor with the total ideal speed given. The two state variables are selected as

$$x_1{}^n = \text{the growth factor of the } n\text{th stage} = G^n$$
$$x_2{}^n = \text{the total ideal speed at the } n\text{th stage} = V^n$$

and the decision variable is

$$\theta^n = \text{the payload ratio of the } n\text{th stage} = \lambda^n$$

With these notations, equations (143) and (146) can be rewritten in the form of equations (1) and (3) for the nth stage

$$x_1{}^n = x_1^{n-1}\theta^n, \qquad\qquad\qquad n = 1, 2, \ldots, N \qquad (147)$$

$$x_2{}^n = x_2^{n-1} - C^n \ln \left(\frac{\theta^n}{1 + \epsilon^n \theta^n} \right), \qquad n = 1, 2, \ldots, N \qquad (148)$$

with the boundary conditions

$$x_1{}^0 = 1$$
$$x_2{}^0 = V \qquad\qquad\qquad (149)$$
$$x_2{}^N = 0$$

It follows that

$$T(x_1^{n-1}; \theta^n) = x_1^{n-1}\theta^n \qquad\qquad (150)$$

$$G(x_1^{n-1}; \theta^n) = -C^n \ln \left(\frac{\theta^n}{1 + \epsilon^n \theta^n} \right) \qquad (151)$$

The problem is formulated as that of finding a sequence of θ^n to minimize $x_1{}^N$, the growth factor.

Partial differentiations of equations (150) and (151) give

$$\frac{\partial T(x_1^{n-1}; \theta^n)}{\partial x_1^{n-1}} = \theta^n \qquad\qquad (152)$$

$$\frac{\partial T(x_1^{n-1}; \theta^n)}{\partial \theta^n} = x_1^{n-1} \qquad\qquad (153)$$

$$\frac{\partial G(x_1^{n-1}; \theta^n)}{\partial x_1^{n-1}} = 0 \qquad\qquad (154)$$

$$\frac{\partial G(x_1^{n-1}; \theta^n)}{\partial \theta^n} = -\frac{C^n}{\theta^n(1 + \epsilon^n \theta^n)} \qquad (155)$$

Substitutions of the preceding four equations into equation (17) yield the following recursion relation

$$\frac{1 + \epsilon^n \theta^n}{C^n} = \frac{1 + \epsilon^{n+1} \theta^{n+1}}{C^{n+1}}, \qquad n = 1, 2, \ldots, N - 1 \qquad (156)$$

from which the optimal sequence of θ^n can be readily computed.

For the simple case where the exhaust speed of the propellant as well as the structure ratio are the same for all the stages,

$$\begin{aligned} C^n &= C, \\ \epsilon^n &= \epsilon, \end{aligned} \qquad n = 1, 2, \ldots, N \qquad (157)$$

The general solution, equation (156), is reduced to

$$\theta^n = \theta, \qquad n = 1, 2, \ldots, N \qquad (158)$$

This is the well-known case of equality of corresponding weight ratios [23]. This simple case is one example of the linear processes which are considered in the next section.

To solve the problem of maximizing the total ideal speed with the growth factor given, the numbering of stages shown in Fig. 13 is reversed so that the problem becomes that of maximizing $x_2{}^N$. The problem then can be solved in a similar way and the result thus obtained is exactly the same as equation (156).

h. Step Rockets II [20]. In the problem treated in Part g, the structure ratio ϵ^n is assumed to be constant at each stage although it may vary from stage to stage. Here, the variations in structural factors with stage weight are considered. A similar problem with different formulation was investigated by Coleman [24] with the use of Lagrangian multipliers.

Let w^n represent the nth stage weight. Then the structural factor for the nth stage σ^n is defined by

$$\sigma^n = \frac{W_s{}^n}{w^n} = \frac{\begin{array}{c}\text{weight of vehicle at cutoff of } n\text{th stage} \\ \text{minus weight of payload of the } n\text{th stage}\end{array}}{\text{the } n\text{th stage weight}}$$

The following scaling law in terms of the weight of the nth stage w^n is assumed to hold

$$\sigma^n = b^n (w^n)^{\gamma^n - 1} \qquad (159)$$

where b^n and γ^n are empirical constants for each stage subject to the selection of propellant, feed system, auxiliary system, etc. The performance equations for a multistage rocket vehicle, equations (143) and (146), still hold. For the present purpose, however, they are expressed in a slightly different manner as follows.

The growth factor

$$G = \frac{\text{launching weight}}{\text{payload weight}} = \frac{W_0{}^N}{W_0{}^0}$$

$$= \frac{1}{w^0} [w^0 + w^1 + w^2 + \cdots + w^N] \qquad (160)$$

where $W_0{}^0 = w^0$ the rocket payload.

The total ideal speed

$$V = \sum_{n=1}^{N} C^n \ln r^n \qquad (146)$$

where

$$r^n = \frac{W_0{}^n}{W_c{}^n} = \frac{w^0 + w^1 + w^2 + \cdots + w^n}{w^0 + w^1 + \cdots + w^{n-1} + b^n(w^n)^{\gamma^n}} \qquad (161)$$

The problem is to obtain the optimal weight distribution to (1) minimize the growth factor G with the total ideal speed V given or (2) maximize the total ideal speed V with the growth factor G given.

As in Part g, let us consider at first the problem of minimizing the growth factor with the total ideal speed given. The two state variables are again selected as

$$x_1{}^n = \text{the growth factor of the } n\text{th stage} = G^n.$$
$$x_2{}^n = \text{the total ideal speed at } n\text{th stage} = V^n.$$

and the decision variable is

$$\theta^n = w^n, \text{ the stage weight of the } n\text{th stage.}$$

Thus equation (160) can be rewritten in the following form:

$$x_1{}^n = x_1^{n-1} + \frac{\theta^n}{w^0}, \qquad x_1{}^0 = 1, \qquad n = 1, 2, \ldots, N \qquad (162)$$

Since

$$w^0 x_1{}^n = w^0 + w^1 + w^2 + \cdots + w^n \qquad (163)$$

equation (161) becomes

$$r^n = \frac{w^0 x_1^{n-1} + \theta^n}{w^0 x_1^{n-1} + b^n(\theta^n)^{\gamma^n}} \qquad (164)$$

From the definition of the state variable x_2 and equations (146) and (164), we formulate the following performance equation:

$$x_2{}^n = x_2^{n-1} - C^n \ln \left[\frac{w^0 x_1^{n-1} + \theta^n}{w^0 x_1^{n-1} + b^n(\theta^n)^{\gamma^n}} \right] \qquad (165)$$

$$x_2{}^0 = V, \qquad x_2{}^N = 0, \qquad n = 1, 2, \ldots, N$$

The problem becomes that of finding the sequence of θ^n to minimize x_1^N.

Comparing equations (162) and (165) with equations (1) and (3), we obtain

$$T(x_1^{n-1}; \theta^n) = x_1^{n-1} + \frac{\theta^n}{w^0} \tag{166}$$

$$G(x_1^{n-1}; \theta^n) = -C^n \ln \left[\frac{w^0 x_1^{n-1} + \theta^n}{w^0 x_1^{n-1} + b^n(\theta^n)^{\gamma^n}} \right] \tag{167}$$

Partial differentiations of these two equations with respect to x_1^{n-1} and θ^n give

$$\frac{\partial T(x_1^{n-1}; \theta^n)}{\partial x_1^{n-1}} = 1 \tag{168}$$

$$\frac{\partial T(x_1^{n-1}; \theta^n)}{\partial \theta^n} = \frac{1}{w^0} \tag{169}$$

$$\frac{\partial G(x_1^{n-1}; \theta^n)}{\partial x_1^{n-1}} = -\frac{C^n w^0 [b^n(\theta^n)^{\gamma^n} - \theta^n]}{(w^0 x_1^{n-1} + \theta^n)[w^0 x_1^{n-1} + b^n(\theta^n)^{\gamma^n}]} \tag{170}$$

$$\frac{\partial G(x_1^{n-1}; \theta^n)}{\partial \theta^n} = -\frac{C^n}{w^0 x_1^{n-1} + \theta^n} + \frac{C^n b^n \gamma^n (\theta^n)^{\gamma^n - 1}}{w^0 x_1^{n-1} + b^n(\theta^n)^{\gamma^n}} \tag{171}$$

Substitution of these expressions into equation (17) yields

$$C^n \left[1 - b^n \gamma^n (\theta^n)^{\gamma^n - 1} \cdot \frac{w^0 x_1^{n-1} + \theta^n}{w^0 x_1^{n-1} + b^n(\theta^n)^{\gamma^n}} \right]$$

$$= \frac{C^{n+1}[1 - b^{n+1}\gamma^{n+1}(\theta^{n+1})^{\gamma^{n+1}-1}]}{1 - b^{n+1}(\theta^{n+1})^{\gamma^{n+1}-1}}$$

$$\times \left[1 - b^{n+1}(\theta^{n+1})^{\gamma^{n+1}-1} \cdot \frac{w^0 x_1^n + \theta^{n+1}}{w^0 x_1^n + b^{n+1}(\theta^{n+1})^{\gamma^{n+1}}} \right] \tag{172}$$

Substituting equations (159) and (164) into equation (172), we have

$$C^{n+1} \frac{(1 - \gamma^{n+1}\sigma^{n+1})}{(1 - \sigma^{n+1})} (1 - \sigma^{n+1} r^{n+1}) = C^n(1 - \gamma^n \sigma^n r^n), \tag{173}$$

$$n = 1, 2, \ldots, N - 1$$

Equation (173) represents the general recurrence relation for N-stage optimal weight distribution of an N-step rocket.

For a three-step rocket vehicle, equation (173) is reduced to

$$C^2 \frac{1 - \gamma^2 \sigma^2}{1 - \sigma^2} (1 - \sigma^2 r^2) = C^1(1 - \gamma^1 \sigma^1 r^1)$$

$$C^3 \frac{1 - \gamma^3 \sigma^3}{1 - \sigma^3} (1 - \sigma^3 r^3) = C^2(1 - \gamma^2 \sigma^2 r^2)$$

which are identical to Coleman's solution [24].

As in Part h, the problem of maximizing the total speed with the growth factor given can be solved in a similar way by reversing the numbering of stages.

4. GENERAL SOLUTION OF LINEAR PROCESSES [25]

It has been mentioned previously that the optimal policy for a linear process described by equations (4) and (5) is to use the same value of decision for all stages. Here we shall show how this simple result can be obtained from the recurrence relation, equation (17). Several examples belonging to this class of process will be discussed in the next section.

Comparing equations (4) and (5) with equations (1) and (3), respectively, we obtain

$$x_1{}^n = T(x_1^{n-1}; \theta^n) = x_1^{n-1}F_1(\theta^n) + \alpha[F_1(\theta^n) - 1] \tag{174}$$

$$G(x_1^{n-1}; \theta^n) = \beta(x_1{}^n - x_1^{n-1}) + F_2(\theta^n), \qquad n = 1, 2, \ldots, N \tag{175}$$

The derivatives of $T(x_1^{n-1}; \theta^n)$ and $G(x_1^{n-1}; \theta^n)$ with respect to x_1^{n-1} and θ^n are readily obtained by straightforward differentiations.

$$\frac{\partial T(x_1^{n-1}; \theta^n)}{\partial \theta^n} = (x_1^{n-1} + \alpha)\frac{dF_1(\theta^n)}{d\theta^n} \tag{176}$$

$$\frac{\partial G(x_1^{n-1}; \theta^n)}{\partial \theta^n} = \beta \frac{dF_1(\theta^n)}{d\theta^n}(x_1^{n-1} + \alpha) + \frac{dF_2(\theta^n)}{d\theta^n} \tag{177}$$

$$\frac{\partial T(x_1^{n-1}; \theta^n)}{\partial x_1^{n-1}} = F_1(\theta^n) \tag{178}$$

$$\frac{\partial G(x_1^{n-1}; \theta^n)}{\partial x_1^{n-1}} = \beta[F_1(\theta^n) - 1] \tag{179}$$

Substituting these expressions into equation (17) gives

$$\beta + \frac{dF_2(\theta^n)/d\theta^n}{[dF_1(\theta^n)/d\theta^n](x_1^{n-1} + \alpha)} = \left[\beta + \frac{dF_2(\theta^{n+1})/d\theta^{n+1}}{[dF_1(\theta^{n+1})/d\theta^{n+1}](x_1{}^n + \alpha)}\right]$$
$$\times F_1(\theta^{n+1}) - \beta[F_1(\theta^{n+1}) - 1]$$

which can be further simplified to

$$(x_1{}^n + \alpha)\frac{dF_1(\theta^{n+1})}{d\theta^{n+1}} \cdot \frac{dF_2(\theta^n)}{d\theta^n}$$
$$= (x_1^{n-1} + \alpha)F_1(\theta^{n+1})\frac{dF_1(\theta^n)}{d\theta^n} \cdot \frac{dF_2(\theta^{n+1})}{d\theta^{n+1}} \tag{180}$$

Substituting equation (174) into equation (180) gives

$$F_1(\theta^n) \cdot \frac{dF_1(\theta^{n+1})}{d\theta^{n+1}} \cdot \frac{dF_2(\theta^n)}{d\theta^n} = F_1(\theta^{n+1}) \cdot \frac{dF_1(\theta^n)}{d\theta^n} \cdot \frac{dF_2(\theta^{n+1})}{d\theta^{n+1}}$$

or

$$\frac{d \ln F_1(\theta^{n+1})/d\theta^{n+1}}{dF_2(\theta^{n+1})/d\theta^{n+1}} = \frac{d \ln F_1(\theta^n)/d\theta^n}{dF_2(\theta^n)/d\theta^n}, \qquad n = 1, 2, \ldots, N - 1$$

from which we conclude that

$$\theta^n = \theta^{n+1}, \qquad n = 1, 2, \ldots, N - 1$$

that is, the values of θ^n are identical throughout the process.

The values for θ^n can be obtained as follows:

(1) For the processes with x_1^N preassigned: solving equation (4) for $F_1(\theta^n)$ gives

$$F_1(\theta) = \frac{x_1^n + \alpha}{x_1^{n-1} + \alpha} \qquad (181)*$$

It follows that

$$\frac{x_1^N + \alpha}{x_1^0 + \alpha} = \frac{x_1^N + \alpha}{x_1^{N-1} + \alpha} \cdot \frac{x_1^{N-1} + \alpha}{x^{N-2} + \alpha} \cdots \frac{x_1^1 + \alpha}{x_1^0 + \alpha} = [F_1(\theta)]^N$$

from which we obtain

$$F_1(\theta) = \left(\frac{x_1^N + \alpha}{x_1^0 + \alpha}\right)^{1/N} \qquad (182)$$

This equation gives the value of θ.

(2) For the process with x_1^N unspecified: let us first consider the feedback process.

Substituting equations (176) through (179) into equation (19) yields

$$\frac{\beta q}{F_1(\theta)} \cdot \frac{dF_1(\theta)/d\theta}{dF_2(\theta)/d\theta} + \frac{q + r}{x_1^N + \alpha} - \frac{r}{x_1^0 + \alpha} = 0 \qquad (183)$$

Thus θ can be obtained by solving equations (2), (182), and (183) simultaneously.

For the simple process with no feedback, equation (183) reduces to

$$\frac{\beta}{F_1(\theta)} \cdot \frac{dF_1(\theta)/d\theta}{dF_2(\theta)/d\theta} + \frac{1}{x_1^N + \alpha} = 0 \qquad (184)$$

5. CASE STUDIES OF LINEAR PROCESSES [25]

In this section, three linear processes which have been treated by others are discussed.

---

* Since all of θ^n, $n = 1, 2, \ldots, N$ are equal, the superscript of θ is removed for simplicity.

a. Multistage Compression of a Gas. The problem of optimal multistage compression of a gas has been solved by Happel [26] using the method of differential calculus and by Aris et al. [27] using the dynamic programming technique.

Here we shall briefly describe the process and show that it belongs to the linear processes.

In an N-stage isentropic compression of a gas from an initial pressure p^0 to a final pressure p^N, it is desired to determine the interstage pressure for which the total energy consumed in compression is the minimum. The gas is cooled isobarically to its initial temperature after each adiabatic compression. The energy consumption at the nth stage is given by

$$E^n = mRT \frac{\gamma}{\gamma - 1} \left[\left(\frac{x_1^{\,n}}{x_1^{n-1}} \right)^{(\gamma-1)/\gamma} - 1 \right] \tag{185}$$

where
 m = the number of moles of gas compressed
 R = the universal gas constant
 T = the initial temperature of the gas
 γ = the ratio of the specific heat of the gas at constant pressure to that at constant volume (assumed constant).
 $x_1^{\,n}$ = pressure of the gas at the end of the nth compression

If we define the decision variable θ^n as

$$\theta^n = \frac{x_1^{\,n}}{x_1^{n-1}} \tag{186}$$

the process can be described by the performance equations

$$x_1^{\,n} = x_1^{n-1}\theta^n, \qquad x_1^{\,0} = p^0, \qquad x_1^{\,N} = p^N \tag{187}$$

$$x_2^{\,n} = x_2^{n-1} + mRT \frac{\gamma}{\gamma - 1} [(\theta^n)^{(\gamma-1)/\gamma} - 1], \qquad x_2^{\,0} = 0 \tag{188}$$

and the problem becomes that of minimizing $x_2^{\,N}$ by the proper choice of θ^n, $n = 1, 2, \ldots, N$.

Comparing equations (187) and (188) with equations (4) and (5), we have

$$\alpha = 0$$

$$\beta = 0$$

$$F_1(\theta^n) = \theta^n$$

$$F_2(\theta^n) = mRT \frac{\gamma}{\gamma - 1} [(\theta^n)^{(\gamma-1)/\gamma} - 1]$$

b.   Stirred Tank Reactors Sequence with an Isothermal First-Order Chemical Reaction.   For the process treated in Section 4.3, Part b, if we use the same temperature in all the stages and the reaction is of the first order such as

$$A \underset{k_2}{\overset{k_1}{\rightleftarrows}} B$$

the rate of reaction at each stage can be written as

$$\frac{dc_B{}^n}{dt} = k_1 c_A{}^n - k_2 c_B{}^n$$

Equation (45) becomes

$$c_B{}^n = c_B^{n-1} + \theta^n (k_1 c_A{}^n - k_2 c_B{}^n)$$

or

$$x_1{}^n = x_1^{n-1} + \theta^n [k_1 (1 - x_1{}^n) - k_2 x_1{}^n] \qquad (189)$$

where

$$x_1 = \frac{c_B}{c_A + c_B}$$

On rearranging, equation (189) becomes

$$x_1{}^n = \frac{x_1^{n-1}}{1 + (k_1 + k_2)\theta^n} - \frac{k_1}{k_1 + k_2}\left[\frac{1}{1 + (k_1 + k_2)\theta^n} - 1\right] \qquad (190)$$

Comparing equations (190) and (49) with equations (4) and (5), we have

$$\alpha = -\frac{k_1}{k_1 + k_2}$$

$$\beta = 0$$

$$F_1(\theta^n) = \frac{1}{1 + (k_1 + k_2)\theta^n}$$

$$F_2(\theta^n) = \theta^n$$

Thus the process is shown to be a linear process. The optimal policy is to use equal volume for all reactors [2].

c.   Multistage Cross-Current Extraction with a Linear Phase Equilibrium Relation.   For the process considered in Section 4.3, Part a, if the phase equilibrium relation is linear, that is,

$$u = \phi(x_1) = \mu x_1$$

equations (21) and (26) become

$$x_1{}^n = \frac{x_1^{n-1}}{1 + \mu\theta^n} \qquad (191)$$

and

$$x_2{}^n = x_2^{n-1} + x_1^{n-1} - x_1{}^n - \lambda\theta^n \tag{192}$$

where θ^n are equivalent to v^n in equations (21) and (26).

Comparing equations (191) and (192) with equations (4) and (5), it is seen that

$$\alpha = 0$$

$$\beta = -1$$

$$F_1(\theta^n) = \frac{1}{1 + \mu\theta^n}$$

$$F_2(\theta^n) = -\lambda\theta^n$$

Thus the process is shown to be linear. The decision variable θ can be obtained for the simple process by equations (182), and (184).

The result is

$$\theta = \left[\frac{x_1{}^f}{(\mu)^N \lambda}\right]^{1/(N+1)} - \frac{1}{\mu}$$

REFERENCES

1. Aris, R., D. F. Rudd, and N. R. Amundson, "On Optimum Cross-Current Extraction," *Chem. Engg. Sci.*, **12**, 88 (1960).
2. Aris, R., *Discrete Dynamic Programming*, Blaisdell Publishing Company, New York, 1963.
3. Rudd, D. F., "Reliability Theory in Chemical System Design," *Ind. Eng. Chem. Fundamentals*, **1**, 138 (1962).
4. Wang, C. S. and L. T. Fan, "Optimization of Some Multistage Chemical Process," *Ind. Eng. Chem. Fundamentals*, **3**, 38 (1964).
5. Fan, L. T. and C. S. Wang, "Optimization of One-Dimensional Multistage Process," *ZAMP*, **15**, 46 (1964).
6. Converse, A. O., "Computer Optimization of a Multistage Allocation Problem by Means of a Non-Imbedding Technique," a paper presented at Chicago Meeting of American Institute of Chemical Engineers, December 1962.
7. Rudd, D. F., and E. D. Blum, "Optimum Cross-Current Extraction with Product Recycle," *Chem. Engg. Sci.*, **17**, 277 (1962).
8. Jackson, R., "Comments on the Paper, Optimum Cross-Current Extraction with Product Recycle," *Chem. Engg. Sci.*, **18**, 215 (1963).
9. Aris, R., *The Optimal Design of Chemical Reactors*, Academic Press, New York, 1961.
10. Ahn, Y. K., H. C. Chen, L. T. Fan, and C. G. Wan, "A Modified Moving Bed Grain Dryer," *I. & E. C. Process Development and Design*, **3**, 96 (1963).
11. Anderson, J. A. and A. W. Alock (Ed.), *Storage of Cereal Grains and Their Products*, Am. Assn. of Cereal Chemists, St. Paul, Minnesota (1954).
12. Henderson, S. H., "Basic Concept of Equilibrium Moisture," *Agricultural Engineering*, **33**, 29 (1952).

13. Boas, A. H., "Optimization via Linear and Dynamic Programming," *Chem. Engg.* **85,** 86 (1963).

14. Fan, L. T., C. L. Hwang, and C. S. Wang, "Optimization of Multistage Heat Exchanger System by the Discrete Maximum Principle," Special Report 43, Eng. Exp. Station, Kansas State Univ., 1964.

15. Westbrook, C. T., "Use This Method to Size Each Stage for Best Operation," *Hydrocarbon Processing and Petroleum Refiner,* **40,** No. 9, 201–206 (September 1961).

16. Fan, L. T., and R. C. Lin, "Optimal Design of a Sequence of Adiabatic Reactors by the Discrete Maximum Principle," unpublished paper (1963).

17. Levenspiel, O., *Chemical Reaction Engineering,* John Wiley, New York, 1962.

18. Konoki, K., "Theory on the Operation and Design of the Most Effective Multistage Reactor," *Kagaku Kogaku* (*Chem. Engg.,* Japan), **21,** No. 7, 408 (1957).

19. Konoki, K., "General Review of Optimization," *Kagaku Kogaku* (*Chem. Engg.,* *Japan*), **27,** 434 (1963).

20. Fan, L. T., C. L. Hwang, and C. S. Wang, "Optimization of Step Rockets by the Discrete Maximum Principle," a paper submitted to *Transaction of ASME,* 1963.

21. Hall, H. H. and E. D. Zambelli, "On the Optimization of Multistage Rockets," *Jet Propulsion,* pp. 463–65 (July 1958).

22. Ragsac, R. V. and P. L. Patterson, "Multistage Rocket Optimization," *ARS Journal,* pp. 450–452 (March 1961).

23. Krause, H. G. L., "General Theory of Multistage Rockets and Performance Theory of an N-Stage Satellite Carrier with a Specific Turning Program," Space Flight Report to the Nation/New York Coliseum, October 9–15, 1961, ARS Preprint 2073–61.

24. Coleman, J. J., "Optimum Stage-Weight Distribution of Multistage Rockets," *ARS Journal,* pp. 259–261 (February 1961).

25. Fan, L. T., and C. S. Wang, "Optimization of One-Dimensional Multistage Linear Processes," A paper submitted to *App. Sci. Res.* for publication (1963).

26. Happel, J., *Chemical Process Economics,* John Wiley, New York, 1958.

27. Aris, R., R. Bellman, and R. Kalaba, "Some Optimization Problems in Chemical Engineering," *Chem. Engg. Progr. Symp.,* Series No. 31, **56,** 95 (1960).

5

Processes with Constraints on Decision Variables

In the previous chapter, we treated a class of one-dimensional processes whose optimal policies can be readily obtained from the recurrence relation of the optimal state and decision.

However, it should be noted that the recurrence relation of the optimal state and decision presented in the previous chapter is applicable only when the stationary points of the Hamiltonian functions lie within the constraints of the decision variables. When the Hamiltonian function is linear in the decision variables, or when the stationary points lie outside the constraints of the decision variables, the optimal decisions are usually found to be at the lower bounds or the upper bounds of the decision variables. For these cases, the conditions $\partial H^n / \partial \theta^n = 0$ are not satisfied and hence the recurrence relation of the optimal state and decision is not applicable. The optimal decision for these cases are to be found from the conditions $H^n = $ maximum (or minimum). It may be noted that the maxima or minima of the Hamiltonian function for these cases do not occur at the stationary points.

In this chapter we shall present several computational procedures which can be used to solve problems when the recurrence relations of the optimal state and decision are not applicable. All such procedures employ one or another of the trial-and-error techniques. The problem of the catalyst replacement is investigated in Section 2 to illustrate the use of such a technique in detail.

Sometimes the computation can be simplified by a certain mathematical analysis, as illustrated in Section 3.

1. GENERAL COMPUTATIONAL PROCEDURES

The following are the four different computational procedures which we found to be very convenient in the optimization of the processes with constraints on decision variables. As we shall illustrate in the next chapter, they can also be applied in optimizing a multidimensional process when the recurrence relation of the optimal state and decision cannot be readily obtained.

a. Guess at the Final Conditions

Step 1.   Formulate the performance equations for each stage. It may be noted that all the state variables and decision variables of the process must be identified before the performance equations can be formulated. Very often a simpler set of performance equations can be obtained by a proper choice of the state and decision variables.

Step 2.   Formulate the recurrence relation for the covariant vector z, and the Hamiltonian function H.

Step 3.   Assign values to all the components of z^N and x^N which are unspecified.

Step 4.   Maximize (or minimize) the Hamiltonian function at the Nth stage. This can be achieved by searching over all possible values of decision variables using any maximum- (or minimum-) seeking methods [1]. Designate the values of the decision variables which give the maximum (or minimum) value of the Hamiltonian function as the optimal decisions at this stage. If the maximum (or minimum) occurs at a stationary point, it can be obtained simply by the condition $\partial H^n / \partial \theta^n = 0$.

Step 5.   Use the values of the optimal decisions at the Nth stage to calculate z^{N-1} and x^{N-1}.

Step 6.   Repeat steps 4 and 5 for every stage until the initial stage is reached.

Step 7.   If the calculated values of x^0 and z^0 check with the specified ones, the problem is solved. If they do not check, repeat the trial calculation starting from step 3.

b. Guess at the Initial Conditions.   This procedure is similar to Procedure

a except that the values of z^0 and x^0, instead of z^N and x^N, which are unspecified, are guessed and the calculated values of x^N and z^N instead of x^0 and z^0 are checked with the specified ones. The calculation proceeds forwards instead of backwards.

c. Back and Forth Calculation.   This is a modified scheme of Procedure b.

At the end of a trial calculation, if the calculated values of x^N and z^N are not equal to the specified ones, instead of guessing different values of unspecified z^0 and x^0 for the next trial calculation, we can calculate the unspecified z^0 and x^0 from the calculated values of decision variables and the specified x^N and z^N by the performance equations and the recurrence relations of the covariant variables and use the values of z^0 and x^0 so obtained to start the next trial calculation. This procedure is used in Section 2.

d.   Guess at the Decision Variables [2].   This is applicable when all values of x^0 are given.

Step 1.   Same as in Procedure *a*.

Step 2.   Same as in Procedure *a*.

Step 3.   Guess a sequence of θ^n, $n = 1, 2, \ldots, N$

Step 4.   Solve the performance equations for x^n, forward from $n = 1$ to $n = N$.

Step 5.   With these x^n, obtain z^n, backward from $n = N$ to $n = 1$, by their recurrence equations.

Step 6.   With those x^n and z^n, compute a new sequence of θ^n from the condition, $H^n = $ maximum or minimum.

Step. 7   Return to step 4 until the new sequence of θ^n is sufficiently close to the preceding sequence.

2. THE PROBLEM OF THE CATALYST REPLACEMENT [3]

In a catalytic reactor, the efficiency of the process gradually decreases as the catalyst gets older, and it eventually reaches a state at which regeneration or replacement of the catalyst is desired. In addition, because of the continuous deactivation of the catalyst, the best operating conditions (such as temperature and flow rate, etc.) change from day to day. The problem is to find the best operating conditions for each day as well as the day best for regenerating or replacing the catalyst so as to obtain the maximum profit. This problem was first solved by Roberts [4] with dynamic programming.

To facilitate comparison, Roberts' [4] notations are followed. Consider a simple endothermic gas-phase catalytic reaction in a tubular reactor where compound A cracks to compounds B and G.

$$A \rightarrow B + G$$

The system depicted in Fig. 1 consists of a reactor and a distillation tower. The unconverted feed material is recycled to the inlet of the reactor. By material balance we have

$$M = CF \tag{1}$$

$$F = M + L \tag{2}$$

where M is the feed rate; C is the fraction converted or simply the conversion; F is the flow rate through the reactor; L is the recycle rate. The conversion is assumed to be expressed as

$$C = a_1 T - a_2 F - a_3 S \tag{3}$$

where the constants a_1, a_2, and a_3 are evaluated from plant data, S represents the state of the system, which is equivalent to the age of catalyst, and is defined as the cumulative flow rate through the catalyst, namely,

$$S = \sum_{n=1}^{n} F^n \tag{4}$$

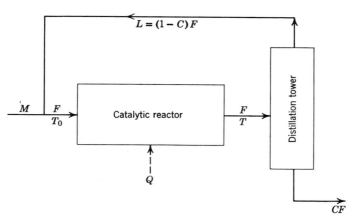

Fig. 1   Schematic flow sheet.

The terms $a_1 T$ and $a_2 F$ evaluate the effect of current exit temperature and flow rate on conversion, whereas the term $a_3 S$ represents the effect due to the cumulative throughput of the feed material.

By energy balance we have

$$Q = FC_p(T - T_0) + HCF \tag{5}$$

where Q is the heat input to the reactor; C_p is the average heat capacity (of the reacting mixture); H is the heat of reaction; T_0 is the temperature of the mixture entering the reactor.

In addition to the relationships represented by equations (3) and (5), the conversion, temperature, and flow rates are subject to the following constraints:

$$C_{\min} \leq C \leq C_{\max} \tag{6}$$

$$T_{\min} \leq T \leq T_{\max} \tag{7}$$

$$F_{\min} \leq F \leq F_{\max} \tag{8}$$

Constraints are placed on conversion to inhibit the formation of undesirable byproducts. The bounds on temperature guarantee that a reaction will take place and that the catalyst will not be ruined by extreme temperatures. The flow rate is constrained because of the limitations on feed availability and plant equipment such as compressors. The temperature and flow-rate combination must be so chosen that equation (6) is satisfied.

The profit obtained per unit time is defined as

$$P = CFV_1 - MV_2 - QV_3 - LV_4 - V_5 \tag{9}$$

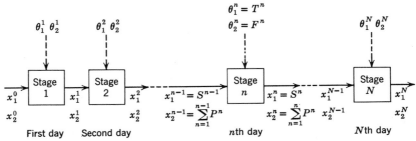

Fig. 2 A multistage scheme for the catalyst replacement problem.

where V_1, V_2, V_3, V_4, and V_5 are the values or costs of each item. Included in V_1 is the combined value of products B and G. V_2 is the cost of the feed. V_3 is the cost of heating. V_4 is the cost of processing the recycle stream through the distillation tower. V_5 accounts for fixed charges.

Subject to relationships of equations (3) and (5) and the constraints represented by equations (6) to (8), it is desired to maximize the profit per unit time P averaged over a period including operation plus shutdown time.

If the whole operation time, that is, the period starting with a new catalyst and continuing until its regeneration, is divided into several time intervals, each being regarded as one stage, the problem becomes a multistage problem as represented by Fig. 2. Here the unit time interval is taken to be one day so that the nth stage corresponds to the nth operating day starting from a fresh catalyst.

To apply the discrete maximum principle, two state variables are defined as

$x_1{}^n$ = the state of the system or the equivalent age of the catalyst at the nth operating day, that is, S at the nth day

$x_2{}^n$ = the cumulative profit starting from the first day until the nth day.

that is, $\sum_{n=1}^{n} P^n$, where P^n is the profit from the nth operating day and two decision variables are defined as

$$\theta_1{}^n = \text{operating temperature } T \text{ at the } n\text{th day}$$
$$\theta_2{}^n = \text{flow rate } F \text{ at the } n\text{th day}$$

Let C^n be the conversion at the nth day; then from equation (3), it can be expressed as

$$C^n = a_1\theta_1{}^n - a_2\theta_2{}^n - a_3 x_1^{n-1}, \qquad n = 1, 2, \ldots, N \qquad (10)$$

The first performance equation is obtained from equation (4) as

$$x_1{}^n = x_1^{n-1} + \theta_2{}^n, \qquad n = 1, 2, \ldots, N \qquad (11)$$

Combining equations (1), (2), (5), and (9) gives the profit obtained at the nth day

$$P^n = C^n\theta_2{}^n(V_1 - V_2) - [\theta_2{}^nC_p(\theta_1{}^n - T_0) + HC^n\theta_2{}^n]V_3$$
$$- (1 - C^n)\theta_2{}^nV_4 - V_5$$

Substituting equation (10) into this equation yields

$$P^n = (a_1\theta_1{}^n - a_2\theta_2{}^n - a_3x_1^{n-1})(V_1 - V_2 - HV_3 + V_4)\theta_2{}^n$$
$$- [C_p(\theta_1{}^n - T_0)V_3 + V_4]\theta_2{}^n - V_5, \qquad n = 1, 2, \ldots, N$$

From the definition of $x_2{}^n$, the second performance equation is obtained as

$$x_2{}^n = x_2^{n-1} + P^n$$

Substituting the expression for P^n into this equation gives

$$x_2{}^n = x_2^{n-1} + (a_1\theta_1{}^n - a_2\theta_2{}^n - a_3x_1^{n-1})(V_1 - V_2 - HV_3 + V_4)\theta_2{}^n$$
$$- [C_p(\theta_1{}^n - T_0)V_3 + V_4]\theta_2{}^n - V_5, \qquad n = 1, 2, \ldots, N \qquad (12)$$

The problem now is transformed into that of finding sequences of $\theta_1{}^n$ and $\theta_2{}^n$ to maximize $x_2{}^N$ for the process described by equations (11) and (12) with the following initial conditions:

$$x_1{}^0 = 0, \qquad x_2{}^0 = 0 \qquad (13)$$

The recurrence relation for the covariant variables are readily obtained from equation (3.22) as

$$z_1^{n-1} = z_1{}^n - a_3(V_1 - V_2 - HV_3 + V_4)\theta_2{}^nz_2{}^n, \qquad (14)$$
$$z_2^{n-1} = z_2{}^n, \qquad n = 1, 2, \ldots, N \qquad (15)$$

The initial and final values of the covariant variables are

$$z_1{}^N = 0 \qquad (16)$$
$$z_2{}^N = 1 \qquad (17)$$

Substituting equation (17) into equation (15) gives

$$z_2{}^n = 1, \qquad n = 0, 1, 2, \ldots, N$$

Following equation (3.21), we obtain the Hamiltonian function from equations (11) and (12) as

$$H^n = z_1{}^n(x_1^{n-1} + \theta_2{}^n) + x_2^{n-1} + (a_1\theta_1{}^n - a_2\theta_2{}^n - a_3x_1^{n-1})$$
$$\times (V_1 - V_2 - HV_3 + V_4) \cdot \theta_2{}^n - [C_p(\theta_1{}^n - T_0)V_3 + V_4]\theta_2{}^n - V_5,$$
$$n = 1, 2, \ldots, N \quad (18)$$

According to the maximum principle algorithm, the optimal sequences of $\theta_1{}^n$ and $\theta_2{}^n$ are determined by the conditions

$$\frac{\partial H^n}{\partial \theta^n} = 0 \quad \text{or} \quad H^n = \text{maximum}, \qquad n = 1, 2, \ldots, N$$

Inspection of equation (18) indicates that the Hamiltonian function H^n is a linear function with respect to $\theta_1{}^n$. Thus the optical decisions at each stage occurs at one point of the boundary and consequently cannot be found by setting $\partial H^n/\partial \theta_1{}^n$ and $\partial H^n/\partial \theta_2{}^n$ equal to zero. However, the maxima of H^n and hence the optimal sequences of $\theta_1{}^n$ and $\theta_2{}^n$ can be evaluated by numerical search as shown in the following numerical example.

For illustration and comparison, the same numerical example presented by Roberts [4] is solved in detail. The following data given by Roberts [4] are used:

$$a_1 = 10^{-3} \qquad V_1 = \$0.10/\text{lb}$$
$$a_2 = 10^{-5} \qquad V_2 = \$0.05/\text{lb}$$
$$a_3 = 10^{-6} \qquad V_3 = \$3.00/\text{million Btu}$$
$$C_p = 0.5 \text{ Btu}/(\text{lb})(°\text{F}) \qquad V_4 = \$0.03/\text{lb}$$
$$H = 300 \text{ Btu/lb} \qquad V_5 = 0$$
$$T_0 = 100°\text{F}$$

The regeneration cost of the catalyst R is \$50.00. It takes one day to regenerate the catalyst. The problem is to find the optimal flow rate F, the optimal temperature T, and the optimal day for regeneration, subject to the constraints

$$5000 \le F(\text{or } \theta_2{}^n) \le 10,000 \text{ lb/day}$$
$$900 \le T(\text{or } \theta_1{}^n) \le 1000°\text{F} \qquad (19)$$
$$0 \le C(\text{or } C^n) \le 0.8$$

which will maximize the profit from the process. The numerical solution is carried out by the general procedure described in Section 1, Part c. Specifically it is carried out as follows.

Step 1. Choose a number N, which is the number of operating days from fresh catalyst to its regeneration (not including the day for regeneration).
Step 2. Assume a value for $z_1{}^0$.
Step 3. Search for $\theta_1{}^n$ and $\theta_2{}^n$ to maximize H^n. This is done as follows:
  (a) Form a grid of $\theta_1{}^1$ and $\theta_2{}^1$, within the constraints of equation (19).

(b) At each node of this grid, compute C^1, x_1^1, x_2^1, z_1^1 and H^1 from equations (10), (11), (12), (14), and (18) in conjunction with the initial condition, equation (13). Select the one which gives the maximum value of H^1 and regard this set of values as $\overline{\theta_1^1}$, $\overline{\theta_2^1}$, $\overline{x_1^1}$, $\overline{x_2^1}$, $\overline{z_1^1}$, and $\overline{H^1}$.

(c) Repeat steps a and b for stages 2, 3, ..., N to obtain the values of $\overline{\theta_1^n}$, $\overline{\theta_2^n}$, $\overline{x_1^n}$, $\overline{x_2^n}$, $\overline{z_1^n}$, and $\overline{H^n}$, $n = 2, 3, \ldots, N$.

Step 4. If $\overline{z_1^N}$ computed is equal to zero as it should be according to equation (16), all the values computed in step 3 are the correct answers. If $z_1^N \neq 0$, calculate z_1^0 from the values of $\overline{\theta_2^n}$ calculated in step 3 by repeatedly applying equation (14).

Step 5. Replace z_1^0 assumed in step 2 by the value of z_1^0 calculated in step 4. The iteration is repeated until $\overline{z_1^N}$ is equal to or sufficiently near zero.

The optimal number of stages N, that is, the optimal number of operating days before catalyst replacement or regeneration, is obtained by repeating the computation described for various values of N. This step can be systematized by the technique described in Chapter II of Wilde's book [1]. The average maximum daily profit (including the day of regeneration) is calculated from

$$P_{\text{average}} = \frac{x_2^N - R}{N + 1} \tag{20}$$

For the numerical example under consideration, it was found that the optimal policy is to operate the process for ten days according to the operating conditions listed in Table 1, and to regenerate the catalyst at the

Table 1 Optimal Operating Policy

Operating Day Counted from New Catalyst	Optimal Flow Rate lb/Day	Optimal Temperature °F
1st	10,000	910
2nd	10,000	920
3rd	10,000	929.6
4th	10,000	940
5th	10,000	949.6
6th	10,000	960
7th	10,000	969.6
8th	10,000	980
9th	10,000	989.6
10th	10,000	1000
11th	Change or regenerate catalyst	

eleventh day. An average maximum daily profit of 314.8 dollars can be realized from the operation. The average maximum daily profits for different numbers of operating days are shown in Fig. 3. The sequence of

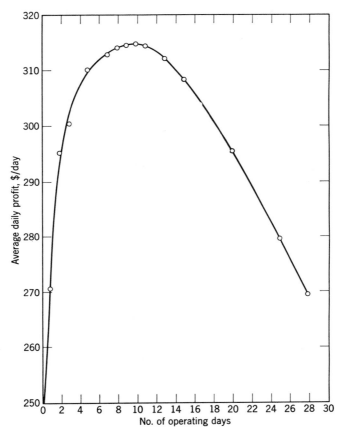

Fig. 3   Maximum average daily profit for different operating days.

optimal operating conditions for the case of $N = 28$ are given in Table 2 to show particularly the effect of prolonged operation.

An IBM 1620 Fortran program was written for this problem. The flow diagram and the source program are given in Fig. 4 and Table 3.

Because of its nonimbedding characteristic, the maximum principle method requires less computing time and hence permits the use of a fine-meshed grid of decision variable space to search for the optimal point. Consequently, it is capable of yielding results more accurate than those obtained by a coarse grid search usually adopted by the dynamic

Table 2. Optimal Operating Conditions for a Twenty-Eight Days' Operating Period

Operating Day	Optimal Flow Rate lb/day	Optimal Temperature °F
1	10,000	910
2	10,000	920
3	10,000	929.6
4	10,000	940
5	10,000	949.6
6	10,000	960
7	10,000	969.6
8	10,000	980
9	10,000	989.6
10	10,000	1000
11	10,000	1000
12	10,000	1000
13	10,000	1000
14	10,000	1000
15	10,000	1000
16	10,000	1000
17	10,000	1000
18	10,000	1000
19	10,000	1000
20	10,000	1000
21	10,000	1000
22	10,000	1000
23	10,000	1000
24	10,000	1000
25	10,000	1000
26	10,000	1000
27	10,000	1000
28	10,000	1000
29	Change or regenerate catalyst	

programming method. In the numerical example solved, a grid of 0.8°C and 40 lb/day was used and a higher profit (that is, a more accurate result) than that calculated by Roberts [4], using a grid of 25°C and 1000

Table 3. Computer Source Program for the Catalyst Replacement Problem

```
       DIMENSION X1(40), X2(40), X3(40), Z2(40), C1(40), C2(40), C10(40)
       DIMENSION C20(40), X10(40), X20(40), X30(40), Z20(40), H(40)
  1    FORMAT (E10.4, I2)
  2    FORMAT (E10.4, E10.4, E10.4)
 10    ACCEPT 1, Z2(1), I
       X1(1) = 0.
       X2(1) = 0.
       X3(1) = 0.
 12    DO 64 N = 1, I
       C1MA = 1000
       C1MI = 900
       C2MA = 10000
       C2MI = 5000
       DC1 = (C1MA − C1MI)/5.
       DC2 = (C2MA − C2MI)/5.
       L = 0
 13    C2(N + 1) = C2MI
       H(N + 1) = −.9999E + 80
       DUM2 = 0.
 16    DUM1 = 0.
       C1(N + 1) = C1MI
 18    X1(N + 1) = 0.001*C1(N + 1) − .1100E − 04*C2(N + 1) − .1000E
                   − 05*X2(N)
       IF(X1(N + 1) − 0.8) 20, 20, 50
 20    IF(X1(N + 1)) 50, 21, 21
 21    X2(N + 1) = X2(N) + C2(N + 1)
       X3(N + 1) = X3(N) + (.0791*X1(N + 1) − .1500E − 05*(C1(N + 1)
                   − 100.) − .03)*C2(N + 1)
       Z2(N + 1) = Z2(N) + .7910E − 07*C2(N + 1)
       HA = Z2(N + 1)*(X2(N) + C2(N + 1)) + X3(N + 1)
       IF(HA − H(N + 1)) 50, 50, 24
 24    H(N + 1) = HA
       C10(N + 1) = C1(N + 1)
       C20(N + 1) = C2(N + 1)
       X10(N + 1) = X1(N + 1)
       X20(N + 1) = X2(N + 1)
       X30(N + 1) = X3(N + 1)
       Z20(N + 1) = Z2(N + 1)
 50    C1(N + 1) = C1(N + 1) + DC1
       DUM1 = DUM1 + 1.
       IF(DUM1 − 6.) 55, 60, 60
 55    GO TO 18
 60    C2(N + 1) = C2(N + 1) + DC2
       DUM2 = DUM2 + 1.
       IF(DUM2 − 6.) 62, 59, 59
```

Table 3   (Continued)

```
62   GO TO 16
59   L = L + 1
     IF(L − 3) 61, 63, 63
61   IF(C10(N + 1) − 900.) 65, 65, 66
65   C1MI = 900.
     GO TO 69
66   IF(C10(N + 1) − 1000.) 67, 68, 68
67   C1MI = C10(N + 1) − 0.5*DC1
     GO TO 69
68   C1MI = C10(N + 1) − DC1
69   IF(C20(N + 1) − 5000.) 77, 77, 78
77   C2MI = 5000.
     GO TO 85
78   IF(C20(N + 1) − 10000.) 79, 80, 80
79   C2MI = C20(N + 1) − 0.5*DC2
     GO TO 85
80   C2MI = C20(N + 1) − DC2
85   DC1 = DC1/5.
     DC2 = DC2/5.
     GO TO 13
63   X1(N + 1) = X10(N + 1)
     X2(N + 1) = X20(N + 1)
     X3(N + 1) = X30(N + 1)
     Z2(N + 1) = Z20(N + 1)
64   PRINT 2, C10(N + 1), C20(N + 1)
     FI = I
     P = (X3(I + 1) − 50.)/FI
     PRINT 2, Z2(I + 1), X3(I + 1), P
     Z20 = 0.
     DO 70 N = 1, 1
70   Z20 = Z20 − .0000000791*C20(N + 1)
     Z2(1) = Z20
     IF (SENSE SWITCH 1) 74, 75
74   GO TO 10
75   GO TO 12
     END
```

lb/day, was obtained. Both results are compared in Table 4 and their differences are plotted in Fig. 5.

The time consumptions for solving this particular problem by both the maximum principle and the dynamic programming technique, using the same grid of 0.8°C and 40 lb/day and an IBM 1620 computer, are recorded and compared in Fig. 6. The time required for the latter is approximately eleven times more than the former.

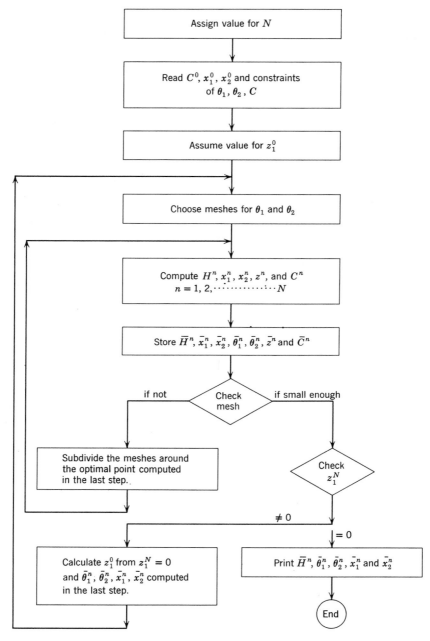

Fig. 4 Computer flow diagram for catalyst replacement problem.

Table 4 A Comparison of the Total Profits Calculated by the Maximum Principle and Dynamic Programming

No. of Operating Days	Total Profit for N Days	
N	By the Maximum Principle—Dollars	By Dynamic Programming—Dollars
1	321	321
2	641.1	634
3	961.1	939
5	1601	1565
7	2240	2197
8	2560	2501
9	2879	2817
10	3198	3125
11	3509	3444
13	4108	4508
15	4676	4640
20	5956	5955

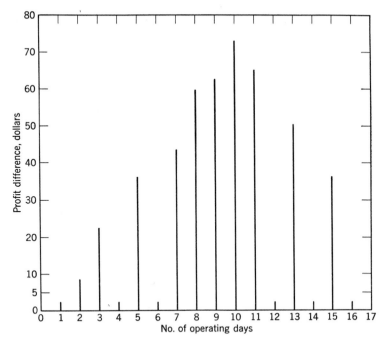

Fig. 5 Differences in profit between the result of Fan et al. and that of Roberts (4).

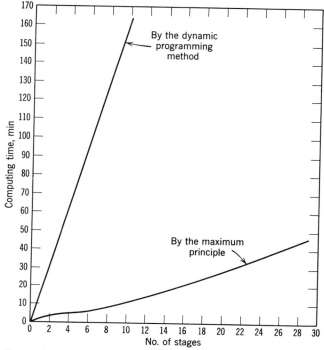

Fig. 6 Comparison of computing time required by dynamic programming and the maximum principle.

3. THE TRANSPORTATION PROBLEM [5]

In this section we wish to present an example for which the computation can be simplified by a certain mathematical analysis.

One of the significant problems in business and industry is that of transporting resources from sources to demand points. One model of this problem which has been extensively examined is the Hitchcock-Koopmans' transportation problem. Using dynamic programming, Bellman [6] treated a realistic model of this general problem in which the cost functions are nonlinear. It was shown by Bellman that the Hitchcock-Koopmans' transportation problem can be treated as an allocation process where the functional equation technique can be applied in conjunction with the Lagrange multiplier or the method of successive approximations. Several numerical examples were solved by these techniques together with the use of digital computers.

Here we shall show that this particular transportation problem can be readily solved by means of the discrete maximum principle. This method works so well in solving such a problem that numerical solutions can often be reached by hand calculations.

Let depots or sources denote the sites where the resources are located and sinks or demand points (markets) denote the sites where the demands for these resources exist.

Suppose that there is only one type of resource and that the total supply is equal to the total demand. Let

$\theta_i{}^n =$ the quantity of the resource sent from the ith depot to the nth demand point

$F_i{}^n(\theta_i{}^n) =$ the cost incurred by this operation

If there are s depots and N demand points, the problem is to determine the quantities of $\theta_i{}^n$, $i = 1, 2, \ldots, s$, $n = 1, 2, \ldots, N$ to minimize the total cost of transporting the resources

$$c_{sN} = \sum_{n=1}^{N} \sum_{i=1}^{s} F_i{}^n(\theta_i{}^n)$$

subject to the constraints

(1) $\theta_i{}^n \geq 0$

(2) $\sum_{n=1}^{N} \theta_i{}^n = W_i$, the supply of the resource available at the ith depot,

$i = 1, 2, \ldots, s$

(3) $\sum_{i=1}^{s} \theta_i{}^n = D^n$, the demand for the resource at the nth demand point,

$n = 1, 2, \ldots, N$

For the problem described, we can write the following performance equations:

$$x_i{}^n = x_i{}^{n-1} + \theta_i{}^n, \qquad x_i{}^0 = 0, \qquad x_i{}^N = W_i$$
$$i = 1, 2, \ldots, s - 1, \qquad n = 1, 2, \ldots, N \quad (21)$$

Here $x_i{}^n$, $i = 1, 2, \ldots, s - 1$ are the state variables representing the total amount of resource which has been transported from the ith depot to the first n demand points. It should be noted that there are only $(s - 1)$ state variables in equation (21) although there are s depots. This arises from the fact that the demand by each sink is preassigned and therefore the supplies from the sth depot can be obtained by subtracting the sum of the supplies of the resource by all the depots except the sth depot, $\sum_{i=1}^{s-1} \theta_i{}^n$, from the total demand for the resource by the nth demand point D^n, that is,

$$\theta_s^n = D^n - \sum_{i=1}^{s-1} \theta_i^n$$

Since it is desired to minimize the total cost of transportation, we define the sth state variable satisfying

$$x_s^n = x_s^{n-1} + \sum_{i=1}^{s} F_i^n(\theta_i^n), \qquad x_s^0 = 0, \qquad n = 1, 2, \ldots, N \qquad (22)$$

It can be readily shown that x_s^N is equal to the total cost of transportation. Now the optimization problem is formulated as one in which x_s^N is to be minimized by the proper choice of θ_i^n, $i = 1, 2, \ldots, s - 1, n = 1, 2, \ldots, N$ for the process described by equations (21) and (22).

Applying equation (3.22) to the transportation problem gives

$$z_i^{n-1} = z_i^n, \qquad i = 1, 2, \ldots, s, \qquad n = 1, 2, \ldots, N \qquad (23)$$

The final value of z_s is obtained from equation (3.23) as

$$z_s^N = 1 \qquad (24)$$

Combining equations (23) and (24) yields

$$z_s^n = 1, \qquad n = 1, 2, \ldots, N \qquad (25)$$

Since the values of x_i^N, $i = 1, 2, \ldots, s - 1$ are prescribed, the values of z_i^N, $i = 1, 2, \ldots, s - 1$ are undetermined at the beginning of calculation. The Hamiltonian function can be written as

$$H^n = \sum_{i=1}^{s-1} z_i^n(x_i^{n-1} + \theta_i^n) + x_s^{n-1} + \sum_{i=1}^{s} F_i^n(\theta_i^n) \qquad (26)$$

The values of θ_i^n, $i = 1, 2, \ldots, s - 1$ are determined in such a way that H^n is the absolute minimum. It should be noted that since z_i^n, $i = 1, 2, \ldots, s - 1$ are undetermined at the beginning of calculation, they play a role similar to the Lagrangian multiplier in differential calculus. The values of z_i^n are to be determined at the end of calculation to make the computed values of x_i^N, $i = 1, 2, \ldots, s - 1$ equal to the given values. For the sake of definiteness, we shall consider a numerical example with two depots and ten demand points. Let us assume that the function $F_i^n(\theta_i^n)$ has the form [6]

$$F_i^n(\theta_i^n) = a_i^n \theta_i^n + b_i^n \cdot (\theta_i^n)^2 + c_i^n(\theta_i^n) \qquad (27)$$

Here a_i^n and b_i^n are constants; $c_i^n(\theta_i^n)$, called a "set-up" cost or "fixed charge," is equal to zero if θ_i^n equals zero and is equal to a positive constant c_i^n for $\theta_i^n > 0$. The values of a_i^n, b_i^n, and c_i^n are shown here [6].

To Sink	From Depot 1			From Depot 2			Demand
n	$a_i{}^n$	$b_i{}^n$	$c_i{}^n$	$a_i{}^n$	$b_i{}^n$	$c_i{}^n$	D^n
1	1.0			3.1		2	10
2	2.0		1	4.1			25
3	3.0	0.01		2.1			45
4	1.5			1.1	0.1		15
5	2.5			2.6			5
6	5.0	−0.01	10	3.0			15
7	3.0			1.0	0.2	5	20
8	6.0			2.0			15
9	6.0	−0.05	8	2.0			10
10	6.0			5.0	0.01		20

The optimal solution for $W_1 = 100$ and $W_2 = 80$ is obtained as follows. Since $z_i{}^n$ and x_i^{n-1} are considered as constants at each step in the minimization of the Hamiltonian function represented by equation (26), it is convenient to define the variable part of the Hamiltonian function as

$$H_v{}^n = \sum_{i=1}^{s-1} z_i{}^n \theta_i{}^n + \sum_{i=1}^{s} F_i{}^n(\theta_i{}^n) \tag{28}$$

Obviously the minimum of H^n is correspondent to the minimum of $H_v{}^n$. For the first sink, we write

$$H_v{}^1 = z_1{}^1 \theta_1{}^1 + [\theta_1{}^1 + 3.1 \cdot (10 - \theta_1{}^1) + c_2{}^1(10 - \theta_1{}^1)]$$

which can be simplified to

$$H_v{}^1 = (z_1{}^1 - 2.1) \cdot \theta_1{}^1 + 31 + c_2{}^1(10 - \theta_1{}^1)$$

It can be seen that the minimum of $H_v{}^1$ occurs at $\theta_1{}^1 = 0$ when $z_1{}^1 > 2.3$, at $\theta_1{}^1 = 10$ when $z_1{}^1 < 2.3$. This can be visualized from the plot of $H_v{}^1$ versus $\theta_1{}^1$ shown in Fig. 7. The minima of H^n for the remaining $(N - 1)$ demand points are obtained in a similar way. The results are summarized in the table on page 94.

The value of z_1 can now be determined by the condition $\sum_{n=1}^{10} \theta_1{}^n = 100$. From the table, it can be readily computed that the conditions are met when $z_1 = -1$. The optimal solution is then obtained by substituting

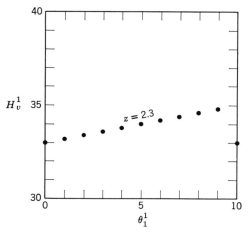

Fig. 7   Plot of H_v^1 versus θ_1^1.

			Minima Occur at	
n	θ_1^n	$z_1{}^a$	θ_1^n	z_1
1	0	$z_1 > 2.3$	10	$z_1 < 2.3$
2	0	$z_1 > 2.06$	25	$z_1 < 2.06$
3	0	$z_1 \geq -0.9$	$-45 - 50z_1$	$-1.8 \leq z_1 \leq -0.9$
	45	$z_1 \leq -1.8$		
4	0	$z_1 \geq 2.6$	$13 - 5z_1$	$-0.4 \leq z_1 \leq 2.6$
	15	$z_1 \leq -0.4$		
5	0	$z_1 > 0.1$	5	$z_1 < 0.1$
6	0	$z_1 > -\frac{151}{60}$	15	$z_1 < -\frac{151}{60}$
7	20	$z_1 \leq 0$	$15 - 2.5z_1$	$0 \leq z_1 \leq 6$
	0	$z_1 \geq 6$		
8	0	$z_1 > -4$	15	$z_1 < -4$
9	0	$z_1 > -4.3$	10	$z_1 < -4.3$
10	20	$z_1 \leq -1$	$-30 - 50z_1$	$-1 \leq z_1 \leq -\frac{3}{5}$
	0	$z_1 \geq -\frac{3}{5}$		

[a] Since the values of z_1 are identical for all stages as indicated by equation (23), the superscripts are omitted for the sake of simplicity.

this value of z_1 into the expressions for $\theta_1{}^n$ in the table. The results are the following.

To Sink	From Depot 1	From Depot 2
1	10	0
2	25	0
3	5	40
4	15	0
5	5	0
6	0	15
7	20	0
8	0	15
9	0	15
10	20	0

An alternative method for the numerical calculation is to guess the values of z_i at the beginning and then compare the computed values of $\sum_{n=1}^{N} \theta_i{}^n$ with the given one after all the numerical values of $\theta_i{}^n$ are determined directly from equation (28) and the guessed values of z_i.

REFERENCES

1. Wilde, D. J., *Optimum Seeking Method*, Prentice-Hall, Englewood Cliffs, New Jersey, 1964.
2. Katz, S., "Best Operating Points for Staged Systems," *Ind. Eng. Chem., Fundamentals*, **1**, 226 (1962).
3. Fan, L. T., C. S. Wang, and R. C. Lin, "The Maximum Principle Formulation of the Catalyst Replacement Problem," unpublished paper, 1963.
4. Roberts, S. M., "Dynamic Programming Formulation of the Catalyst Replacement Problem," *Chem. Eng. Prog. Symposium*, Series 31, **56**, 103–110 (1960).
5. Fan, L. T., and C. S. Wang, "The Application of the Discrete Maximum Principle to Transportation Problem," a paper accepted for publication by *J. Math. Physics*, 1963.
6. Bellman, R. E., and S. E. Dreyfus, *Applied Dynamic Programming*, Princeton Univ. Press, New Jersey, 1962.

6

Multidimensional Processes

When a process has two or more primary state variables, it is called a multidimensional process. It is clear that the optimization problems become more complicated as the dimension increases. In general, it is difficult, often impossible, to obtain the recurrence relation of the optimal state and decision for a multidimensional process as for a one-dimensional process described in Chapter 4. Therefore the optimization problem of a multidimensional process is usually solved by the trial-and-error method as used in solving the optimization problem of a process with constraints on decision vector as presented in the previous chapter.

In Section 1, we present a process with three state variables for which a recurrence relation of the optimal decision can be derived. The use of the trial-and-error method in treating the complicated multidimensional processes is illustrated in the later sections.

1. THE MIMIMUM WEIGHT OF STEP ROCKETS [1]

The step rocket optimization problem treated in Section 4.3 is now considered with the objective of minimizing the total cost. Under the condition of nonrecovery of stages, a better approximation of the least cost may be obtained by minimizing hardware weight instead of launch weight. The problem is to find the optimum weight distribution of the multistage rocket vehicle to minimize the hardware weight.

In addition to the notations introduced in Section 4.3, we define an nth stage structure coefficient S^n as

$$S^n = \frac{\text{total structure weight of first } n \text{ stages}}{\text{payload weight}}$$

$$= \frac{\sum\limits_{n=0}^{n} \epsilon^n W_0^n}{W_0^0}$$

where ϵ^n is the structure ratio and $\epsilon^0 = 1$.

The structure coefficient can be given in terms of payload ratios λ^n as follows:

$$S^n = \frac{1}{W_0^0} \sum_0^n \epsilon^n W_0^n$$

$$= \sum_0^n \epsilon^n \lambda^0 \lambda^1 \lambda^2 \cdots \lambda^n \tag{1}$$

where $\lambda^0 = 1$.

Equation (1) serves as one of the performance equations. The performance equation associated with the total ideal speed is identical to equation (4.146).

$$V = \sum_{n=1}^{N} C^n \ln r^n \tag{2}$$

where

$$r^n = \frac{\lambda^n}{1 + \epsilon^n \lambda^n} \tag{3}$$

The problem is to obtain the optimum weight distribution for minimizing the total structure coefficient S^N. The decision variable for this problem is the payload ratio of each stage.

Three state variables and one decision variable are defined as follows.

$x_1^n = $ the total structure coefficient at the nth stage $= S^n$

$x_2^n = $ the total ideal speed at the nth stage $= V^n$

$$x_3^n = \prod_{n=0}^n \lambda^n$$

$\theta^n = $ the payload ratio of the nth stage $= \lambda^n$

From equations (1) and (2), we can readily derive the following performance equations.

$$x_1^n = x_1^{n-1} + \epsilon^n x_3^{n-1} \theta^n \tag{4}$$

$$x_2^n = x_2^{n-1} - C^n \ln \frac{\theta^n}{1 + \epsilon^n \theta^n} \tag{5}$$

$$x_3^n = x_3^{n-1} \theta^n, \qquad n = 1, 2, \ldots, N \tag{6}$$

The boundary conditions are

$$x_1{}^0 = 1 \tag{7}$$

$$x_2{}^N = 0, \qquad x_2{}^0 = V \tag{8}$$

$$x_3{}^0 = 1 \tag{9}$$

The problem is now transformed into that of finding a sequence of θ^n to minimize the total structure coefficient $x_1{}^N$.

According to the maximum principle, the recurrence relations for the components of covariant vector z can be readily obtained as

$$z_1^{n-1} = z_1{}^n \tag{10}$$

$$z_2^{n-1} = z_2{}^n \tag{11}$$

$$z_3^{n-1} = z_1{}^n \epsilon^n \theta^n + \theta^n z_3{}^n, \qquad n = 1, 2, \ldots, N \tag{12}$$

and the final values are

$$z_1{}^N = 1, \qquad z_3{}^N = 0 \tag{13}$$

Therefore

$$z_1{}^n = 1, \qquad n = 1, 2, \ldots, N \tag{14}$$

The Hamiltonian function is

$$H^n = x_1^{n-1} + \epsilon^n x_3^{n-1} \theta^n + z_2{}^n \left(x_2^{n-1} - C^n \ln \frac{\theta^n}{1 + \epsilon^n \theta^n} \right) + z_3{}^n x_3^{n-1} \theta^n,$$

$$n = 1, 2, \ldots, N \tag{15}$$

The optimal sequence of θ^n is determined so that

$$H^n = \text{minimum}, \qquad n = 1, 2, \ldots, N \tag{16}$$

or

$$\frac{\partial H^n}{\partial \theta^n} = 0 \tag{17}$$

if the optimal decisions occur at stationary point. Applying equation (17) to equation (15) gives the following relation:

$$z_2{}^n = \frac{\theta^n (1 + \epsilon^n \theta^n)}{C^n} (z_3{}^n x_3^{n-1} + \epsilon^n x_3^{n-1}) \tag{18}$$

Inserting equation (18) into equation (11), we obtain

$$\frac{\theta^{n-1}(1 + \epsilon^{n-1}\theta^{n-1})}{C^{n-1}} (z_3^{n-1} x_3^{n-2} + \epsilon^{n-1} x_3^{n-2})$$

$$= \frac{\theta^n (1 + \epsilon^n \theta^n)}{C^n} (z_3{}^n x_3^{n-1} + \epsilon^n x_3^{n-1}), \qquad n = 1, 2, \ldots, N \tag{19}$$

Substituting equation (12) into equation (19) and then solving the resulting equation for $z_3{}^n$, we obtain

$$z_3{}^n = -\epsilon^n + \frac{C^n \epsilon^{n-1} \theta^{n-1} r^n}{\theta^n(\theta^n C^{n-1} r^{n-1} - \theta^{n-1} C^n r^n)} \tag{20}$$

Insertion of equation (20) into equation (12) gives

$$\frac{\epsilon^{n-1}\theta^n}{\theta^n C^{n-1} r^{n-1} - \theta^{n-1} C^n r^n} = \frac{\epsilon^{n-2}\theta^{n-2}}{\theta^{n-1}(\theta^{n-1} C^{n-2} r^{n-2} - \theta^{n-2} C^{n-1} r^{n-1})} \tag{21}$$

Equation (21) gives the recurrence relation among the parameters C^n, ϵ^n, r^n, and the decision variable θ^n for the optimal weight distribution.

For the special case where the exhaust speed of the propellant as well as the structure ratio are identical for all the stages, that is,

$$\left.\begin{array}{c} C^n = C \\ \epsilon^n = \epsilon \end{array}\right\}, \quad n = 1, 2, \ldots, N$$

the recurrence relation, equation (21), is reduced to

$$\frac{\theta^n}{\theta^n r^{n-1} - \theta^{n-1} r^n} = \frac{\theta^{n-2}}{\theta^{n-1}(\theta^{n-1} r^{n-2} - \theta^{n-2} r^{n-1})} \tag{22}$$

For a three-stage rocket vehicle, equation (22) gives

$$\frac{\theta^3}{\theta^3 r^2 - \theta^2 r^3} = \frac{\theta^1}{\theta^2(\theta^2 r^1 - \theta^1 r^2)}$$

2. A STAGEWISE BIOCHEMICAL REACTOR SYSTEM [2]

In many biochemical reactions, catalysts are enzymes of protein origin [3]. Although the catalytic behavior of an enzyme is quite complicated, the two most influential factors on the activity of the enzyme are temperature and pH value. An increase of temperature or pH value will enhance the activity of the enzyme, but, beyond a certain extent, the enzyme would be deactivated by further increase of temperature or pH value. This feature of biochemical reactions is different from that of nonbiochemical reactions whose specific reaction rates change according to the Arrhenius rate expression. The fact that there exists an optimum condition for the enzyme activity is well-known [3, 4]. Although the exact functions of the activity versus temperature and pH value should be acquired under actual operating conditions, the general form may be represented by the unimodal curves similar to those shown in Fig. 1. The curves correspond to the following particular hypothetical functions [4]:

$$k(\theta) = -3(\theta)^2 + 10\theta + 12, \qquad 4 \geq \theta \geq 0 \tag{23}$$

$$h(\theta) = -(\theta)^2 + 9\theta - 6, \qquad 7 \geq \theta \geq 1 \tag{24}$$

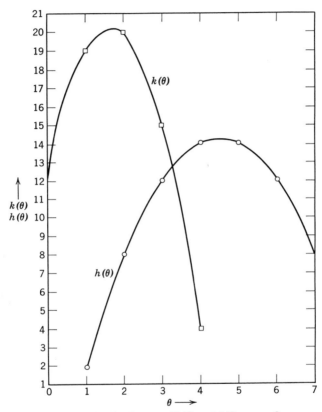

Fig. 1   Curves of $k(\theta)$ and $h(\theta)$ versus θ.

where θ is the variable representing either temperature or pH value, $h(\theta)$ and $k(\theta)$ are the activities of enzymes.

The following consecutive biochemical reaction system will be considered:

$$A \xrightarrow[\text{enzyme 1}]{k(\theta)} B \xrightarrow[\text{enzyme 2}]{h(\theta)} C$$

where A is an expensive raw material, B is an intermediate product of no commercial value, and C is the desired product. This reaction is fairly common in the fermentation processes. Some of the examples are listed in Table 1 [4]. The enzyme indicated is the catalyst for each reaction. Some of the reactions are of commercial importance.

Suppose that the consecutive reaction is to be carried out in a series of completely mixed reactors with equal volume. The problem is to find an optimal decision sequence θ^n to maximize the production of C for a fixed input of A.

Table 1 Some Examples of Consecutive Biochemical Reactions [4]

1. Celluloses	$\xrightarrow{\text{Cellulase}}$	Cellobiose	$\xrightarrow{\text{Cellobiase}}$	Glucose
2. Maltose / Trehalose	$\xrightarrow{\text{Maltase}}$ / $\xrightarrow{\text{Trehalase}}$	Glucose	$\xrightarrow{\text{Zymase}}$	Alcohol + CO_2
3. Insulin	$\xrightarrow{\text{Insulase}}$	Fructose	$\xrightarrow{\text{Zymase}}$	Alcohol + CO_2
4. Albumoses / Peptones / Peptides	$\xrightarrow{\text{Erepsin}}$	Amino acid	$\xrightarrow{\text{Desaminases}}$	Hydroxy-acids + Ammonia
5. Xanthine	$\xrightarrow{\text{Xanthoxides}}$	Uric acid	$\xrightarrow{\text{Uricolase}}$	Allantoin
6. Sucrose	$\xrightarrow{\text{Invertase}}$	Fructose + Glucose	$\xrightarrow{\text{Zymase}}$	Alcohol + CO_2

The feed rate is maintained constant, and thus the residence time t in each reactor is also constant. In what follows, a general process with N reactors is first considered and then a three-stage process with $t = 0.01$ is numerically solved.

The concentrations of A, B, and C denoted by x_1, x_2, and x_3 respectively are the state variables, and the temperature or the pH value, denoted by θ, is the decision variable. Here, we are considering only one decision variable. The reactors have the identical volume of V and the volumetric flow rate of the stream v is constant throughout the system. It is assumed that there is no density change in the process, which is generally true for liquid phase reactions.

Since the reaction under consideration is a first-order consecutive reaction, the kinetic equations for the rates of the appearance of A, B, and C can be expressed by

$$r_A = -k(\theta)x_1$$
$$r_B = k(\theta)x_1 - h(\theta)x_2$$
$$r_C = h(\theta)x_2$$

The material balance around the nth stage with respect to the component A is

$$vx_1^{n-1} = vx_1^n + (-r_A)V$$

Replacing r_A by $-k(\theta)x_1$ and V/v by t, we obtain

$$x_1^{n-1} = x_1^n + tk(\theta^n)x_1^n$$

Solving for x_1^n, we have

$$x_1^n = \frac{x_1^{n-1}}{1 + k(\theta^n)t} \tag{25}$$

Similarly, material balances for B and C give

$$x_2^n = \left[x_2^{n-1} + \frac{k(\theta^n)x_1^{n-1}t}{1 + k(\theta^n)t} \right] \Big/ [1 + h(\theta^n)t] \tag{26}$$

and

$$x_3^n = x_3^{n-1} + h(\theta^n)t\left[x_2^{n-1} + \frac{k(\theta^n)x_1^{n-1}t}{1 + k(\theta^n)t} \right] \Big/ [1 + h(\theta^n)t] \tag{27}$$

The problem is to maximize x_3^N with the initial conditions

$$x_1^0 = a$$
$$x_2^0 = b \tag{28}$$
$$x_3^0 = c$$

Applying the maximum principle algorithm, we obtain the following set of equations for the covariant variables:

$$z_1^{n-1} = \frac{z_1^n}{1 + k(\theta^n)t} + \frac{tk(\theta^n)[z_2^n + h(\theta^n)z_3^n t]}{[1 + k(\theta^n)t][1 + h(\theta^n)t]} \tag{29}$$

$$z_2^{n-1} = \frac{z_2^n + h(\theta^n)tz_3^n}{1 + h(\theta^n)t} \tag{30}$$

$$z_3^{n-1} = z_3^n \tag{31}$$

The final conditions for z_i are

$$z_i^N = \begin{cases} 1, & i = 3 \\ 0, & i \neq 3 \end{cases} \tag{32}$$

Substituting equation (32) into equations (29) through (31) yields

$$z_3^n = 1 \tag{33}$$

$$z_2^{n-1} = \frac{z_2^n + h(\theta^n)t}{1 + h(\theta^n)t} \tag{34}$$

$$z_1^{n-1} = \frac{[1 + h(\theta^n)t]z_1^n + k(\theta^n)t[z_2^n + h(\theta^n)t]}{[1 + h(\theta^n)t][1 + k(\theta^n)t]} \tag{35}$$

The Hamiltonian function is formulated as

$$H^n = \frac{x_1^{n-1}z_1^{n}}{1 + k(\theta^n)t} + [z_2^{n} + h(\theta^n)t]$$

$$\times \left[x_2^{n-1} + \frac{k(\theta^n)tx_1^{n-1}}{1 + k(\theta^n)t} \right] \Big/ [1 + h(\theta^n)t] + x_3^{n-1} \quad (36)$$

The following substitutions are made to simplify the presentation.

$$F(\theta^n) = \frac{k(\theta^n)t}{1 + k(\theta^n)t} \qquad G(\theta^n) = \frac{h(\theta^n)t}{1 + h(\theta^n)t}$$

$$F_1(\theta^n) = \frac{dF(\theta^n)}{d\theta^n} \qquad G_1(\theta^n) = \frac{dG(\theta^n)}{d\theta^n}$$

The Hamiltonian function becomes

$$H^n = x_1^{n-1}z_1^{n}[1 - F(\theta^n)] + [x_2^{n-1} + F(\theta^n)x_1^{n-1}]$$

$$\times \{z_2^{n}[1 - G(\theta^n)] + G(\theta^n)\} + x_3^{n-1} \quad (37)$$

The optimal decision θ^n may be determined by the following equation:

$$\frac{\partial H^n}{\partial \theta^n} = -x_1^{n-1}z_1^{n}F_1(\theta^n) + F_1(\theta^n)x_1^{n-1}\{z_2^{n}[1 - G(\theta^n)] + G(\theta^n)\}$$

$$+ [x_2^{n-1} + F(\theta^n)x_1^{n-1}][G_1(\theta^n) - z_2^{n}G_1(\theta^n)] = 0 \quad (38)$$

However, it has been found, for this particular example, that it is more convenient to obtain the optimal θ^n by directly searching the maximum of H^n with the use of a digital computer. Of course, when the stationary points of H^n lies outside of the range of θ^n, the maxima-seeking methods must always be used.

The procedure described in Section 5.1, Part d, is used in solving a three-stage process. With the given values of the initial concentrations, $x_1^{0} = 1$, $x_2^{0} = 0.3$, and $x_3^{0} = 0$, a set of θ^1, θ^2, and θ^3 is arbitrarily chosen. x_i^{n} are then calculated by equations (25), (26), and (27) and z_i^{n} by equations (34) and (35). With these values of x_i^{n} and z_i^{n}, a new set of θ^1, θ^2, and θ^3 is obtained from the condition $H^n = $ maximum by any maximum-seeking method. This new set of decisions is employed to calculate the x_i^{n} and z_i^{n} and again a set of θ^1, θ^2, and θ^3. The procedure is stopped when two consecutive sets of decisions are sufficiently close. Table 2 shows the detail of calculation.

The machine calculation from the first guess to the final answer required less than half an hour when θ^n ranges from 1.0 to 4.5 with an increment of 0.1. Table 2 shows that θ and x_3 converge very rapidly and that the results of two different first guesses are identical. An IBM 1620 digital computer with 20,000 memories was used to carry out these computations.

Table 2   The Results of Iteration Calculation:
Initial Concentrations $x_1^0 = 1$, $x_2^0 = 0.3$, $x_3^0 = 0$

1. First guessing $\theta^1 = 2.5$, $\theta^2 = 3.0$, $\theta^3 = 3.5$

	θ^1	θ^2	θ^3	x_3^3
First calculation	2.6	3.0	3.5	0.16097
Second calculation	2.6	3.0	3.5	0.16097

2. First guessing $\theta^1 = 4.0$, $\theta^2 = 4.0$, $\theta^3 = 4.0$

First calculation	2.6	2.8	3.3	0.12290
Second calculation	2.7	3.0	3.5	0.15999
Third calculation	2.6	3.0	3.5	0.16096
Fourth calculation	2.6	3.0	3.5	0.16097
Fifth calculation	2.6	3.0	3.5	0.16097

3. DENBIGH'S SYSTEM OF REACTIONS

In the First European Symposium on Chemical Reaction Engineering, Denbigh [5] demonstrated that, if the following system of chemical reactions

$$A + B \xrightarrow{k_1} X \xrightarrow{k_3} Y$$
$$\downarrow{k_2} \qquad \downarrow{k_4}$$
$$P \qquad\quad Q$$

is carried out in a sequence of reactors, a great improvement in yield of the desired product Y can result when optimal policies are adopted.

In this system of reactions, X is an intermediate and P and Q are the products of side reactions. The raw material A is expensive, whereas the raw material B is cheap and is available in excess amount for reaction. This system of reactions comprises a general class of reactions which are frequently encountered in the manufacturing chemical industry. All the reactions in this system are taken to be first order with respect to the concentration of A and X. The reaction rate constants of the four reactions are of the usual Arrhenius form

$$k_i = k_{i0} e^{-E_i/RT}, \qquad i = 1, 2, 3, 4$$

Four different cases distinguished by the relative magnitude of the activation energy arise [6].

1. $E_1 > E_2$, $E_3 > E_4$. For this case it can be readily seen that a conversion of nearly all A to Y is expected with a sufficiently high operating temperature.

2. $E_1 < E_2$, $E_3 < E_4$. For this case, it is apparent that the lowest allowable temperature will give the best yield.

3. $E_1 > E_2$, $E_3 < E_4$. In the early stages of the reaction, the concentration of X is still low, therefore temperature should be high to promote the production of X. As soon as the quantity of X becomes considerable, the temperature should be lowered to prevent the side reaction. Hence a decreasing sequence of temperature is desirable.

4. $E_1 < E_2$, $E_3 > E_4$. In this case an argument similar to that in 3 calls for an increasing temperature sequence.

The optimal policies for the first two cases are simply to use the highest and the lowest allowable temperature, respectively. It is the third and the fourth cases whose optimizations need mathematical analysis. Case 4 was originally considered by Denbigh [5], using the method of differential calculus. He obtained the result that the greatest yield of Y is increased from 25% of the feed A when a single reactor is used, to 57% when two reactors in series are used. Employing the method of dynamic programming, Aris [6] made a study of the same problem as well as three reactors in series. The effect of restrictions on the temperature and holding time was also considered in his work.

By means of the discrete maximum principle, Wan [7] solved the same problem and showed that results were much better than those obtained by the dynamic programming algorithm for two and three reactors in series with restrictions on temperature and holding time.

The following is a solution of the problem by the maximum principle [7].

Suppose that this system of reactions is carried out in a sequence of N completely stirred reactors connected in series. We are seeking to maximize the yield of Y with given feed. Let x_1, x_2, and x_3 denote the concentrations of A, X, and Y respectively and ρ the residence time in each stage. The material balance around the nth stage yields

$$x_1^{n-1} = x_1^n[1 + \rho^n(k_1^n + k_2^n)]$$
$$x_2^{n-1} = -x_1^n\rho^n k_1^n + x_2^n[1 + \rho^n(k_3^n + k_4^n)]$$
$$x_3^{n-1} = -x_2^n\rho^n k_3^n + x_3^n$$

If the values of the specific reaction rates given by Denbigh [5] are used,

$$\frac{k_2}{k_1} = 10^4 e^{-3000/T}$$

$$\frac{k_3}{k_1} = 10^{-2}$$

$$\frac{k_4}{k_3} = 10^{-4} e^{3000/T}$$

and the following substitutions are made:

$$\theta = \frac{k_2}{k_1} = 10^4 e^{-3000/T} \tag{39}$$

$$t = \rho k_1$$

the material balance around the nth stage of a process consisting of N completely stirred tank reactors becomes

$$x_1^{n-1} = [1 + t^n(1 + \theta^n)]x_1^n \tag{40}$$

$$x_2^{n-1} = -t^n x_1^n + [1 + 0.01t^n(\theta^n)^{-1}(1 + \theta^n)]x_2^n \tag{41}$$

$$x_3^{n-1} = -0.01t^n x_2^n + x_3^n \tag{42}$$

Solving equations (40) through (42) for $x_i{}^n$, $i = 1, 2, 3$, we have

$$x_1{}^n = \frac{x_1^{n-1}}{1 + t^n(1 + \theta^n)} \tag{43}$$

$$x_2{}^n = \frac{x_2^{n-1} + t^n\left[\dfrac{x_1^{n-1}}{1 + t^n(1 + \theta^n)}\right]}{1 + 0.01t^n(1 + \theta^n)/\theta^n} \tag{44}$$

$$x_3{}^n = x_3^{n-1} + 0.01t^n\left\{\frac{\left[x_2^{n-1} + t^n\dfrac{x_1^{n-1}}{1 + t^n(1 + \theta^n)}\right]}{1 + 0.01t^n(1 + \theta^n)/\theta^n}\right\} \tag{45}$$

The problem is to maximize $x_3{}^N$ with the initial conditions

$$x_1{}^0 = 1$$
$$x_2{}^0 = 0 \tag{46}$$
$$x_3{}^0 = 0$$

Applying the maximum principle algorithm, we obtain the following recurrence relations for the components of the covariant vector:

$$z_1^{n-1} = \frac{z_1{}^n}{1 + t^n(1 + \theta^n)} + \frac{t^n z_2{}^n}{[1 + t^n(1 + \theta^n)][1 + 0.01t^n(1 + 1/\theta^n)]}$$

$$+ \frac{0.01 z_3{}^n(t^n)^2}{[1 + t^n(1 + \theta^n)][1 + 0.01t^n(1 + 1/\theta^n)]}$$

$$z_2^{n-1} = \frac{z_2{}^n}{1 + 0.01t^n(1 + 1/\theta^n)} + \frac{0.01t^n z_3{}^n}{1 + 0.01t^n(1 + 1/\theta^n)}$$

$$z_3^{n-1} = z_3{}^n$$

The boundary conditions for z_i are

$$z_i^N = \begin{cases} 1, & i = 3 \\ 0, & i = 1, 2 \end{cases}$$

It follows that

$$z_3^n = 1, \qquad n = 1, 2, \ldots, N \tag{47}$$

$$z_2^{n-1} = \frac{z_2^n}{1 + 0.01t^n(1 + 1/\theta^n)} + \frac{0.01t^n}{1 + 0.01t^n(1 + 1/\theta^n)} \tag{48}$$

$$z_1^{n-1} = \frac{z_1^n}{1 + t^n(1 + \theta^n)} + \frac{t^n z_2^n}{[1 + t^n(1 + \theta^n)][1 + 0.01t^n(1 + 1/\theta^n)]}$$

$$+ \frac{0.01(t^n)^2}{[1 + t^n(1 + \theta^n)][1 + 0.01t^n(1 + 1/\theta^n)]} \tag{49}$$

The Hamiltonian function can be written as

$$H^n = \frac{x_1^{n-1} z_1^n}{1 + t^n(1 + \theta^n)} + \left[\frac{x_2^{n-1} + \dfrac{x_1^{n-1} t^n}{1 + t^n(1 + \theta^n)}}{1 + 0.01t^n(1 + 1/\theta^n)} \right] [z_2^n + 0.01t^n] + x_3^{n-1}$$

The optimal decisions are to be determined from the conditions

$$H^n = \text{maximum}, \qquad n = 1, 2, \ldots, N \tag{50}$$

The computational procedure for solving this problem is exactly the same as the one used in solving the biochemical problem in the last section.

The amount of computing time, dependent linearly on the number of stages, is almost independent of the number of state variables. Although the time used in calculation for the two-stage process was about two hours, the amount of time would largely depend on the searching range and searching grid of the two decision variables. The time required is approximately proportional to the products of the number of increments of the two decision variables t^n and θ^n used in search. Actually, a proper choice of the searching grid could make the calculation of a three-stage process possible in half an hour without too much sacrifice in accuracy.

The numerical results thus obtained are given in Table 3. For comparison, Aris's results are listed in Table 4. It can be seen that they are very close when there is no constraint on the decision variables. But when there are restrictions, the results do show considerable differences for the two-stage and the three-stage processes. The lower yields calculated by the dynamic programming method might have resulted from the interpolation error.

Table 3 Wan's Results for Denbigh's System of Reactions Calculated by the Maximum Principle Algorithm [7]

Number of Reactors,	Temperature, °K			"Holding Times"[a]			Yield of Y
N	T^1	T^2	T^3	t^1	t^2	t^3	(% of feed A)
With no restriction on temperature and holding time							
1	326	–	–	∞	–	–	25
2	279.9	∞	–	4.55	∞	–	57.99
3	267.4	295	∞	1.7	2.6	∞	66.55
With restrictions on temperature and holding time							
1	310	–	–	340	–	–	22
2	278.8	394	–	3.85	2100	–	49.03
3	265	292	394	1.35	2.35	2100	54.84

[a] The holding times are given as values of $t = \rho k_1$ and cannot be translated into the actual holding time without assuming values for k_{10} and E_1.

Table 4 Aris's Results for Denbigh's System of Reaction Calculated by the Dynamic Programming Algorithm [6]

Number of Reactors,	Temperature, °K			"Holding Times"[a]			Yield of Y
N	T^1	T^2	T^3	t^1	t^2	t^3	(% of feed A)
With no restrictions on temperature and holding time							
1	326	–	–	∞	–	–	25
2	280	∞	–	4.0	∞	–	57.4
3	270	320	∞	1.6	0.8	∞	66.3
With restrictions on temperature and holding time							
1	318	–	–	340	–	–	22.1
2	276	394	–	2.82	2100	–	45.1
3	260	288	394	1.4	1.3	2100	49.5

[a] See footnote in Table 3

4. THE ADIABATIC REACTOR SEQUENCE [8]

In this section, the optimal design of a sequence of adiabatic non-catalytic tubular reactors where an exothermic reaction is carried out is considered.

The problem is similar to the one treated in Section 4.3, Part f, except that the profit instead of the total volume of the process is considered as the objective function in this case.

For simplicity, a first-order reversible exothermic reaction is discussed. The reaction can be represented as follows,

$$\underset{\substack{C_A \\ =C_{A0}-y}}{A} \overset{k_1}{\underset{k_2}{\rightleftarrows}} \underset{\substack{C_B \\ =C_{B0}+y}}{B}, \quad K = \frac{k_1}{k_2}$$

where k_1, k_2 are the specific reaction rates; C_{A0}, C_{B0} are the initial concentrations of the compounds A and B; y is the conversion, that is, the number of moles of A converted per unit volume, and K is the equilibrium constant.

For a plug flow tubular reactor, we have

$$r\, dV = F\, dy$$

or

$$\frac{V^n}{F} = \tau^n = \int_{y^{n-1}}^{y^n} \frac{dy}{r} \tag{51}$$

where F is the volumetric flow rate through the reactor, V is the reactor volume, τ is the space time, n refers to the nth stage, and r is the rate of reaction defined as

$$r = \frac{dC_B}{dS}$$

where S represents time.

The reaction rate of a first-order reversible reaction can be expressed as

$$r = k_1 C_A - k_2 C_B$$

or

$$r = k_2[K(C_{A0} - y) - C_{B0} - y] \tag{52}$$

Substituting the Arrhenius' expression

$$k_2 = k_{20} e^{-E/RT}$$

and the thermodynamic relationship

$$K = K_0 e^{-(\Delta H/R)(1/t - 1/T_0)}$$

into equation (52), we obtain

$$r = k_{20} e^{-E/RT}[K_0 e^{-(\Delta H/R)(1/t-1/T_0)}(C_{A0} - y) - C_{B0} - y] \tag{53}$$

where E is the activation energy, ΔH is the heat of reaction, and K_0 is the equilibrium constant at the temperature T_0.

For an adiabatic reaction the energy balance equation for the nth stage is

$$C_p(t - t_0^n) = -\Delta H(y - y^{n-1}) \tag{54}$$

where C_p is the average heat capacity per unit volume of the reaction mixture, $t_0{}^n$ is the temperature corresponding to a conversion y, and y^{n-1} is the conversion leaving the $(n-1)$th stage or entering the nth stage.

By substituting equation (54) into equation (53), the reaction rate can be expressed as a function of $t_0{}^n$, y^{n-1}, and y as

$$r = k_{20} \exp\left\{-\frac{E}{R[t_0{}^n - (\Delta H/C_p)(y - y^{n-1})]}\right\}$$

$$\times K_0 \exp\left\{-\frac{\Delta H}{R}\left[\frac{1}{t_0{}^n - (\Delta H/C_p)(y - y^{n-1})} - \frac{1}{T_0}\right]\right\}(C_{A0} - y) - C_{B0} - y$$

or

$$r = \frac{1}{f(t_0{}^n, y^{n-1}, y)} \tag{55}$$

Substituting equation (55) into equation (51) yields

$$\tau^n = \int_{y^{n-1}}^{y^n} f(t_0{}^n, y^{n-1}, y)\, dy \tag{56}$$

Suppose that the profit per unit time for the process is defined as

$$P = F(C_A{}^N V_a + C_B{}^N V_b) - F(C_{A0} V_a + C_{B0} V_b)$$
$$- \sum_{n=1}^{N} C_p(t^{n-1} - t_0{}^n) F V_h - V_r \sum_{n=1}^{N} V^n$$

where V_a and V_b are the unit prices of compounds A and B, V_h is the cooling cost per unit amount of heat, and V_r is the reactor cost per unit volume. The first two terms account for the profit from the product, the third term accounts for the cooling cost, and the fourth term for the reactor cost. The profit function can be rewritten as

$$P = F(V_b - V_a)\sum_{n=1}^{N}(y^n - y^{n-1}) - C_p F V_h \sum_{n=1}^{N}(t^{n-1} - t_0{}^n) - F V_r \sum_{n=1}^{N} \tau^n \tag{57}$$

Now the problem is to find the sequences of $t_0{}^n$ and τ^n to maximize the net profit P.

Three state variables are identified as (see Fig. 2)

x_1:   conversion, that is, y

x_2:   temperature of the reaction mixture at the outlet of each stage, that is, t

x_3:   cumulative profit from the first stage to the nth stage

Two decision variables are identified as

θ_1:   temperature of the reaction mixture entering each stage, that is, t_0

θ_2:   space time of each stage, that is, τ

With these notations, three performance equations are obtained from equations (54), (56), and (57) as

$$\theta_2{}^n = \int_{x_1^{n-1}}^{x_1^n} f(\theta_1{}^n, x_1^{n-1}, y)\, dy, \qquad n = 1, 2, \ldots, N \tag{58}$$

$$x_2{}^n = \theta_1{}^n - \frac{\Delta H}{C_p}(x_1{}^n - x_1^{n-1}), \qquad n = 1, 2, \ldots, N \tag{59}$$

$$x_3{}^n = x_3^{n-1} + F[(x_1{}^n - x_1^{n-1})(V_b - V_a) + C_p(\theta_1{}^n - x_2^{n-1})V_h - \theta_2{}^n V_r],$$
$$n = 1, 2, \ldots, N \tag{60}$$

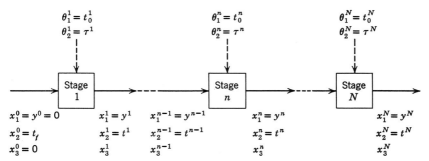

Fig. 2 A simplified multistage adiabatic reactor scheme.

The three initial conditions are

$$x_1{}^0 = 0 \tag{61}$$
$$x_2{}^0 = t_f \tag{62}$$
$$x_3{}^0 = 0 \tag{63}$$

where t_f is the temperature of the feed. Now the optimization problem is transformed into that of finding the sequences of $\theta_1{}^n$ and $\theta_2{}^n$ to maximize $x_3{}^N$ for the process described by equations (58) through (63).

The recurrence relations and the final values for the components of the covariant vector z for the problem are obtained as

$$z_1^{n-1} = z_1{}^n \frac{\partial x_1{}^n}{\partial x_1^{n-1}} + z_2{}^n \frac{\Delta H}{C_p}\left(1 - \frac{\partial x_1{}^n}{\partial x_1^{n-1}}\right) + F(V_b - V_a)\left(\frac{\partial x_1{}^n}{\partial x_1^{n-1}} - 1\right),$$
$$n = 1, 2, \ldots, N \tag{64}$$

$$z_1{}^N = 0 \tag{65}$$
$$z_2{}^n = -FC_p V_h, \qquad n = 0, 1, 2, \ldots, N - 1 \tag{66}$$
$$z_2{}^N = 0 \tag{67}$$
$$z_3{}^n = 1, \qquad n = 0, 1, 2, \ldots, N \tag{68}$$

The term $\partial x_1^n / \partial x_1^{n-1}$ is found by differentiation of equation (58) with respect to x_1^{n-1} as

$$\frac{\partial x_1^n}{\partial x_1^{n-1}} = \frac{1}{f(\theta_1^n, x_1^{n-1}, x_1^n)}\left[f(\theta_1^n, x_1^{n-1}, x_1^n) - \int_{x_1^{n-1}}^{x_1^n} \frac{\partial f(\theta_1^n, x_1^{n-1}, y)}{\partial x_1^{n-1}}\, dy \right]$$

From equation (3.5), the Hamiltonian function for this problem is found to be

$$H^n = z_1^n x_1^n + z_2^n\left[\theta_1^n - \frac{\Delta H}{C_p}(x_1^n - x_1^{n-1}) \right] + x_3^{n-1}$$
$$+ F[(x_1^n - x_1^{n-1})(V_b - V_a) + C_p(\theta_1^n - x_2^{n-1})V_h - \theta_2^n V_r],$$
$$n = 1, 2, \ldots, N \quad (69)$$

The optimal sequences of θ_1^n and θ_2^n are to be found by setting $\partial H^n / \partial \theta_1^n$ and $\partial H^n / \partial \theta_2^n$ equal to zero. By this we have

$$\left[z_1^n - \frac{\Delta H}{C_p} z_2^n + F(V_b - V_a) \right]\frac{\partial x_1^n}{\partial \theta_1^n} + z_2^n + FC_p V_h = 0,$$
$$n = 1, 2, \ldots, N \quad (70)$$

$$\left[z_1^n - \frac{\Delta H}{C_p} z_2^n + F(V_b - V_a) \right]\frac{\partial x_1^n}{\partial \theta_2^n} - FV_r = 0, \qquad n = 1, 2, \ldots, N$$
$$(71)$$

The two terms, $\partial x_1^n / \partial \theta_1^n$ and $\partial x_1^n / \partial \theta_2^n$, are found from equation (58) to be

$$\frac{\partial x_1^n}{\partial \theta_1^n} = -\frac{1}{f(\theta_1^n, x_1^{n-1}, x_1^n)}\int_{x_1^{n-1}}^{x_1^n} \frac{\partial f(\theta_1^n, x_1^{n-1}, y)}{\partial \theta_1^n}\, dy$$

$$\frac{\partial x_1^n}{\partial \theta_2^n} = \frac{1}{f(\theta_1^n, x_1^{n-1}, x_1^n)}$$

The optimal sequences of θ_1^n and θ_2^n can now be obtained by any computational procedure described in Section 5.1.

It may be noted that the number of stages N is regarded as a variable in the preceding treatment. By simply repeating the trial-and-error calculations for several values of N, we can find the optimal number of stages which gives the greatest maximum profit. This procedure can be readily systematized [9].

REFERENCES

1. Fan, L. T., C. L. Hwang, and C. S. Wang, "Optimization of Step Rockets by the Discrete Maximum Principle," a paper submitted to *Trans. ASME* for publication, 1963.

2. Fan, L. T. and C. G. Wan, "An Application of the Discrete Maximum Principle to a Stagewise Biochemical Reactor System," *Biotechnology and Bioengineering*, **5**, 201 (1963).

3. Laidler, K. J., *The Chemical Kinetics of Enzyme Action*, Oxford University Press, London, 1958.

4. Waksman, S. A. and W. C. Davison, *Enzymes*, The Williams & Wilkins Company, Baltimore, 1926.

5. Dehbign, K. C., "Optimal Temperature Sequences in Reactors," *Chem. Eng. Sci.*, **8**, 125 (1958).

6. Aris, R., *The Optimal Design of Chemical Reactors*, Academic Press, New York, 1961.

7. Wan, C. G., M. S. report, Kansas State University, 1963.

8. Fan, L. T. and R. C. Lin, unpublished paper.

9. Wilde, D. J., *Optimum Seeking Method*, Prentice-Hall, Englewood Cliffs, New Jersey, 1964.

7

The Generalized Discrete Maximum Principle

In this chapter, a generalized algorithm for the optimization of any types of multistage processes is presented. As it is well known, many of the processes encountered in practice, especially in chemical industry, belong to the complex processes. Although very often the optimal policy for a complex process can be obtained by dissecting the process into several rather simple subprocesses, independently optimizing each subprocess and then combining together the optimal policies for all the subprocesses, it is desirable to derive an algorithm capable of obtaining directly the optimal policy for the entire process without decomposing the process. This chapter presents such an algorithm. It is also shown that the particular algorithm presented in Chapter 3 for the simple feedback process can be reduced from this general algorithm.

1. STATEMENT OF THE ALGORITHM [1]

The algorithm stated in this section is applicable to a complex process consisting of all four basic types of stages and any number of initial and final stages. For examples of the complex processes, see Fig. 1.2.

The optimization problem under consideration can be stated as follows. Given all the performance equations for a process, it is desired to find the value of a decision vector at each stage, subject to certain constraints, to maximize the objective function which is a certain function of the state vector leaving the last stages. All the values of the state vector entering the initial stages and leaving the last stages are unspecified.

It may be felt that this problem is somewhat narrow. However, by means of the techniques described in Section 3.4 a wide variety of problems can be reduced to this standard form. It may also be noted that, for the problem of minimizing instead of maximizing the objective function, we simply replace the word "maximum" by the word "minimum" in the algorithm given here.

Let an *s*-dimensional vector x represent the state vector, and a *t*-dimensional vector θ stand for the decision vector. The set of performance equations for a linking stage* is of the form

$$x^n = T^n(x^{n-1}; \theta^n) \tag{1}$$

For a separating stage

$$x^{m'} = T^{m'}(x^{m-1}; \theta^m)$$
$$x^{m''} = T^{m''}(x^{m-1}; \theta^m) \tag{2}$$

For a combining stage

$$x^n = T^n(x^{(n-1)'}; x^{(n-1)''}; \theta^n) \tag{3}$$

For a complex stage

$$x^{n'} = T^{n'}(x^{(n-1)'}; x^{(n-1)''}; \theta^n)$$
$$x^{n''} = T^{n''}(x^{(n-1)'}; x^{(n-1)''}; \theta^n) \tag{4}$$

To find the optimal sequence of the decision vector, we introduce a covariant vector z and a Hamiltonian function H satisfying the following.

1. For a linking stage

$$z^{n-1} = \frac{\partial H^n}{\partial x^{n-1}} \tag{5}$$

$$H^n = \sum_{i=1}^{s} z_i{}^n T_i{}^n(x^{n-1}; \theta^n) \tag{6}$$

2. For a separating stage

$$z^{m-1} = \frac{\partial H^m}{\partial x^{m-1}} \tag{7}$$

$$H^m = \sum_{i=1}^{s'} z_i{}^{m'} T_i{}^{m'}(x^{m-1}; \theta^m) + \sum_{i=1}^{s''} z_i{}^{m''} T_i{}^{m''}(x^{m-1}; \theta^m) \tag{8}$$

---

* See Fig. 1.1 for the four basic types of stages. For simplicity, we just consider a separating stage consisting of one entering stream and two leaving streams, a combining stage consisting of two entering streams and one leaving stream, and a complex stage consisting of two entering and two leaving streams. It is obvious that the algorithm can be readily extended to the separating stage consisting of one entering stream and several leaving streams and so on.

3. For a combining stage

$$z^{(n-1)'} = \frac{\partial H^n}{\partial x^{(n-1)'}} \tag{9}$$

$$z^{(n-1)''} = \frac{\partial H^n}{\partial x^{(n-1)''}} \tag{10}$$

$$H^n = \sum_{i=1}^{s} z_i{}^n T_i{}^n(x^{(n-1)'}; x^{(n-1)''}; \theta^n) \tag{11}$$

4. For a complex stage

$$z^{(n-1)'} = \frac{\partial H^n}{\partial x^{(n-1)'}} \tag{12}$$

$$z^{(n-1)''} = \frac{\partial H^n}{\partial x^{(n-1)''}} \tag{13}$$

$$H^n = \sum_{i=1}^{s'} z_i{}^{n'} T_i{}^{n'}(x^{(n-1)'}; x^{(n-1)''}; \theta^n)$$
$$+ \sum_{i=1}^{s''} z_i{}^{n''} T_i{}^{n''}(x^{(n-1)'}; x^{(n-1)''}; \theta^n) \tag{14}$$

The optimal decisions at these stages are then determined by the following conditions:

$$\frac{\partial H^n}{\partial \theta^n} = 0 \quad \text{or} \quad H^n = \text{maximum} \tag{15}$$

In the maximization of the Hamiltonian function, both x and z are considered as fixed at each stage.

The values of $z_i{}^0$ and $z_i{}^N$ are determined by

$$z_i{}^0 = 0 \quad \text{or} \quad x_i{}^0 z_i{}^0 = \text{maximum} \tag{16}$$

$$z_i{}^N = \frac{\partial \phi(x^N)}{\partial x_i{}^N} \tag{17}$$

where $\phi(x^N)$ is the objective function.

It may be noted that equations (2), (3), and (4) are of the same form as equation (1), and hence can be replaced by the latter if we allow the state vector to have its appropriate dimension for each type of stages. The same is true for the defining equations of the covariant vector and the Hamiltonian function, equations (5) through (14).

From the definition of the covariant vector, it can be seen that there is always one component of z corresponding to one component of x. The specifications of the values of $z_i{}^0$ and $z_i{}^N$ are also dependent on those of x. Thus, to solve the problem in which the initial and/or final values of some x_i are prescribed, the conditions given in equations (16) and (17) for the corresponding $z_i{}^0$ and/or $z_i{}^N$ should be deleted.

2. THE DERIVATION OF THE ALGORITHM

We shall derive the generalized discrete maximum principle for a process consisting of all the four basic types of stages but with only one initial stage and one final stage. The algorithm thus derived can be applied to processes with any number of initial and final stages. The derivation is given for the case of maximizing the objective function, with the value of all the state variables entering the initial stage and leaving the final stage unspecified. The derivation for the case of minimizing the objective function can be obtained by simply reversing the direction of the inequality sign.

Let $\overline{x^0}$ represent the optimal values of x^0, and $\overline{x^n}$, $n = 1, 2, \ldots, N$ represent the state resulting from the optimal sequence of decisions $\overline{\theta^n}$, $n = 1, 2, \ldots, N$; then

$$\overline{x^n} = T^n(\overline{x^{n-1}}; \overline{\theta^n}) \qquad \text{for the linking stage}$$
$$\overline{x^m} = T^m(\overline{x^{m-1}}; \overline{\theta^m}) \qquad \text{for the separating stage} \qquad (18)$$

$$\overline{x^n} = T^n(\overline{x^{(n-1)'}}; \overline{x^{(n-1)''}}; \overline{\theta^n}) \qquad \text{for the combining stage}$$
$$\overline{x^{n'}} = T^{n'}(\overline{x^{(n-1)'}}; \overline{x^{(n-1)''}}; \overline{\theta^n})$$
$$\overline{x^{n''}} = T^{n''}(\overline{x^{(n-1)'}}; \overline{x^{(n-1)''}}; \overline{\theta^n}) \qquad \text{for the complex stage} \qquad (19)$$

If the following independent small perturbations are made on the decision vector at each stage and on the state vector entering the initial stage

$$\theta^n = \overline{\theta^n} + \epsilon\phi^n, \qquad n = 1, 2, \ldots, N \qquad (20)$$

$$x^0 = \overline{x^0} + \epsilon y^0 \qquad (21)$$

The disturbance will alter $\overline{x^n}$ to

$$x^n = \overline{x^n} + \epsilon y^n + O(\epsilon^2), \qquad n = 1, 2, \ldots, N \qquad (22)$$

Here ϵ is a positive parameter which is of the first-order smallness; $O(\epsilon^2)$ denotes both vector and scalar quantities which are of a smallness of a higher order than ϵ; ϕ^n is a t-dimensional vector and y^n is an s-dimensional vector, both being independent of ϵ.

For the linking and the separating stages, a recurrence relation for y can be obtained by combining equations (1), (2), (18), and (22) and then expanding the resulting equation in powers of ϵy. The result is

$$\epsilon y_i^n = \sum_{j=1}^{s} \epsilon y_j^{n-1} \frac{\partial T_i^n(\overline{x^{n-1}}; \overline{\theta^n})}{\partial x_j^{n-1}} + T_i^n(\overline{x^{n-1}}; \theta^n) - T_i^n(\overline{x^{n-1}}; \overline{\theta^n}) + O(\epsilon^2),$$
$$i = 1, 2, \ldots, s \qquad (23)$$

Similarly, for the combining and the complex stages, we obtain the following relation from equations (3), (4), (19), and (22)

$$\epsilon y_i{}^n = \sum_{j=1}^{s'} \epsilon y_j^{(n-1)'} \frac{\partial T_i{}^n(\overline{x^{(n-1)'}}; \, x^{(n-1)''}; \, \overline{\theta^n})}{\partial \overline{x_j^{(n-1)'}}} + \sum_{j=1}^{s''} \epsilon y_j^{(n-1)''}$$

$$\cdot \frac{\partial T_i{}^n(\overline{x^{(n-1)'}}; \, x^{(n-1)''}; \, \overline{\theta^n})}{\partial \overline{x_j^{(n-1)''}}} + T_i{}^n(\overline{x^{(n-1)'}}; \, \overline{x^{(n-1)''}}; \, \overline{\theta^n})$$

$$- T_i{}^n(\overline{x^{(n-1)'}}; \, \overline{x^{(n-1)''}}; \, \overline{\theta^n}) + O(\epsilon^2) \quad (24)$$

Multiplying equations (23) and (24) by $z_i{}^n$ and summing over all the stages and all the components of the state vector yield

$$\epsilon \sum_{i=1}^{s} y_i{}^N z_i{}^N = \sum_{n=1}^{N} \sum_{i=1}^{s} z_i{}^n [T_i{}^n(\overline{x^{n-1}}; \, \theta^n) - T_i{}^n(\overline{x^{n-1}}; \, \overline{\theta^n})]$$

$$+ \epsilon \sum_{i=1}^{s} y_i{}^0 z_i{}^0 + O(\epsilon^2) \quad (25)$$

Here $z_i{}^n$ and $T_i{}^n(x^{n-1}; \theta^n)$ are used in their generalized senses as noted in Section 1.

The perturbations of the state vector entering the initial stage and the decision vector change the value of the objective function from $\phi(\overline{x^N})$ to $\phi(x^N)$. Expanding $\phi(x^N)$ in powers of ϵy^N, we have

$$\phi(x^N) - \phi(\overline{x^N}) = \epsilon \sum_{i=1}^{s} y_i{}^N \frac{\partial \phi(\overline{x^N})}{\partial x_i{}^N} + O(\epsilon^2) \quad (26)$$

Since $\overline{x_i{}^0}$, $i = 1, 2, \ldots, s$ and $\overline{\theta^n}$, $n = 1, 2, \ldots, N$ are the optimal values that maximize $\phi(x^N)$, the effect of the perturbations represented by equations (20) and (21) can only be to make

$$[\phi(x^N) - \phi(\overline{x^N})] \le 0 \quad (27)$$

Combining and expanding the resulting equation in terms of $\epsilon \phi$ give equations (17), (25), (26), and (27)

$$\left\{ \sum_{n=1}^{N} \sum_{j=1}^{t} (\epsilon \phi_j{}^n) \sum_{i=1}^{s} z_i{}^n \frac{\partial T_i{}^n(\overline{x^{n-1}}; \, \overline{\theta^n})}{\partial \overline{\theta_j{}^n}} + \epsilon \sum_{i=1}^{s} y_i{}^0 z_i{}^0 + O(\epsilon^2) \right\} \le 0 \quad (28)$$

Since the perturbed decision vector, θ^n, $n = 1, 2, \ldots, N$ and the perturbed state vector entering the initial stage, $x_i{}^0$, $i = 1, 2, \ldots, s$ are independent of each other, it may be concluded that each term of equation (28) containing a set of independent variables θ^n or $x_i{}^0$ must itself be nonpositive. Thus

$$\sum_{j=1}^{t} (\overline{\theta_j{}^n} - \overline{\theta_j{}^n}) \sum_{i=1}^{s} z_i{}^n \frac{\partial T_i{}^n(\overline{x^{n-1}}; \, \overline{\theta^n})}{\partial \overline{\theta_j{}^n}} \le 0, \qquad n = 1, 2, \ldots, N$$

and
$$y_i^0 z_i^0 \leq 0, \qquad i = 1, 2, \ldots, s$$
which are equivalent to equations (15) and (16), respectively. This completes the derivation of the general algorithm.

To solve the optimization problem with some x_i^0 and/or x_i^N preassigned, we simply delete the conditions given in equations (16) and (17) for the corresponding components of z. This modification can be readily verified by observing that the corresponding y_i^0 and y_i^N are not included in equation (25), and consequently the specifications of the corresponding z_i^0 and z_i^N in equations (16) and (17) are redundant.

3. SIMPLE FEEDBACK PROCESSES

A special case of feedback loops is the simple feedback processes shown in Fig. 1.2*b*. The widespread occurrence of the simple feedback processes in the chemical industry has stimulated a considerable amount of interest in the study of the optimization of such processes. A particular algorithm for optimizing such processes has been derived in Chapter 3. It will be shown here that such particular algorithm can be readily reduced from the general principle derived in the previous section.

The performance equations for all the stages in a simple feedback process can be written in the form of equation (1). The combination of the feed and the recycle stream is described by the mixing operator

$$x^0 = M(x^f; x^N) \qquad (29)$$

where x^f is the state vector in the feed stream and x^N is the state vector in the recycle or feedback stream. The optimization problem is to maximize $\sum_{i=1}^{s} c_i x_i^N$, with x^f given. The particular algorithm for solving such a problem is to introduce an s-dimensional covariant vector z and a Hamiltonian function H satisfying

$$z^{n-1} = \frac{\partial H^n}{\partial x^{n-1}}, \qquad\qquad n = 1, 2, \ldots, N \qquad (30)$$

$$H^n = \sum_{i=1}^{s} z_i^n T_i^n(x^{n-1}; \theta^n), \qquad n = 1, 2, \ldots, N \qquad (31)$$

$$z_i^N - \sum_{j=1}^{s} z_j^0 \frac{\partial M_j(x^f; x^N)}{\partial x_i^N} = c_i, \qquad i = 1, 2, \ldots, s \qquad (32)$$

and to determine the optimal sequence of the decision vector from the conditions

$$\frac{\partial H^n}{\partial \theta^n} = 0 \quad \text{or} \quad H^n = \text{maximum}, \qquad n = 1, 2, \ldots, N \qquad (33)$$

It can be seen that the particular algorithm differs from the general algorithm only in the specifications of the initial and final conditions of z, that is, equation (32) is different from equations (16) and (17). Now we shall show that equation (32) of the particular algorithm can be derived from equations (16) and (17) of the general algorithm.

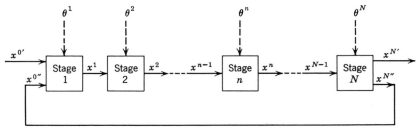

Fig. 1 Simple feedback process.

If we depict the simple feedback process as that shown in Fig. 1, which is obviously equivalent to the one shown in Fig. 1.2*b*, we can write the following performance equations for the initial and the final stages:

$$x^1 = T^1(x^{0'}; x^{0''}; \theta^1) \tag{34}$$

$$x^{N'} = T^N(x^{N-1}; \theta^N) \tag{35}$$

$$x^{N''} = T^N(x^{N-1}; \theta^N) \tag{36}$$

Applying equation (10) to the initial stage in Fig. 1 gives

$$z_i^{0''} = \sum_{j=1}^{s} z_j^1 \frac{\partial T_j^1(x^{0'}; x^{0''}; \theta^1)}{\partial x_i^{0''}} \tag{37}$$

By using equations (29) and (30) and noting that $x^{0''} = x^{N'} = x^{N''} = x^N$ and $x^{0'} = x^f$, we can transform the right-hand side of equation (37) as

$$\sum_{j=1}^{s} z_j^1 \frac{\partial T_j^1(x^{0'}; x^{0''}; \theta^1)}{\partial x_i^{0''}} = \sum_{j=1}^{s} \left[z_j^1 \sum_{k=1}^{s} \frac{\partial T_j^1(x^0; \theta^1)}{\partial x_k^0} \cdot \frac{\partial M_k(x^f; x^N)}{\partial x_i^N} \right]$$

$$= \sum_{k=1}^{s} \left[\frac{\partial M_k(x^f; x^N)}{\partial x_i^N} \sum_{j=1}^{s} z_j^1 \frac{\partial T_j^1(x^0; \theta^1)}{\partial x_k^0} \right]$$

$$= \sum_{k=1}^{s} z_k^0 \frac{\partial M_k(x^f; x^N)}{\partial x_i^N} = \sum_{j=1}^{s} z_j^0 \frac{\partial M_j(x^f; x^N)}{\partial x_i^N}$$

Hence equation (37) can be rewritten as

$$z_i^{N''} = \sum_{j=1}^{s} z_j^0 \frac{\partial M_j(x^f; x^N)}{\partial x_i^N} \tag{38}$$

where $z_i^{0''}$ is replaced by $z_i^{N''}$ since they are identical. Application of equation (7) to the final stage in Fig. 1 yields

$$z_i^{N-1} = \sum_{j=1}^{s} (z_j^{N'} + z_j^{N''}) \cdot \frac{\partial T_j^N(x^{N-1}; \theta^N)}{\partial x_i^{N-1}} \tag{39}$$

Writing equation (30) for the final stage in Fig. 1.2*b* gives

$$z_i^{N-1} = \sum_{j=1}^{s} z_j^N \frac{\partial T_j^N(x^{N-1}; \theta^N)}{\partial x_i^{N-1}} \tag{40}$$

Comparing equation (39) with equation (40), we immediately see that

$$z_j^N = z_j^{N'} + z_j^{N''} \tag{41}$$

The values of $z_j^{N'}$ are obtained from equation (17) as

$$z_j^{N'} = c_j \tag{42}$$

Substitution of equations (38) and (42) into equation (41) gives

$$z_i^N - \sum_{j=1}^{s} z_j^0 \frac{\partial M_j(x^f; x^N)}{\partial x_i^N} = c_i$$

which is exactly the same as equation (32).

REFERENCE

1. Fan, L. T. and C. S. Wang, "Multistage Optimization by the Generalized Discrete Maximum Principle," to appear in *J. Electron. Contr.*, 1964.

8

General Remarks on the Maximum Principle and Dynamic Programming

In this concluding chapter we wish to present several general remarks on the maximum principle and dynamic programming. It is widely recognized that there is at present no single mathematical optimization technique superior to all other techniques in handling every type of problems. Every method has its own merits and shortcomings; consequently, it may be suitable in solving some types of problems but become cumbersome in solving others. Remembering that we are dealing with the optimization of a process, and "optimizing a process" is itself a process, we would be absent-minded if we forgot to optimize what we are doing. The problem now facing us is to choose the most adequate technique to solve a specific type of problem. For some problems, the best method may be to use several techniques jointly, as was illustrated by Lee [1]. In order to do so, a comparative study of all available techniques is necessary. Since dynamic programming and the maximum principle are generally regarded as the two most powerful in solving problems of a stagewise nature, we shall restrict our discussion to these two techniques. Those readers who are not familiar with the notion of dynamic programming may find it helpful to read Appendices 2 and 3 before proceeding.

A number of papers and books [2 through 6] in which the relationship between dynamic programming and the maximum principle is discussed have been published. Many of them have presented detailed derivation of one method from the other and hence have concluded that these two methods are essentially the same. However, it is important to note that the ultimate object of optimization is not the formulations of the problems and the methods for solving them, but is the numerical solution of the optimal policy which can be immediately used. Although dynamic programming and the maximum principle can be derived from each other, which obviously must be true or otherwise one of them would be incorrect, the ways of approach to the problems according to each method are quite different. The difference becomes more evident when problems are solved numerically. Lee [7] has given a comparison between the calculation philosophies of the two methods in optimizing an m-stage process with n state variables.

Dynamic programming will start the investigation by searching the entire grid of the n variables at one stage, store this grid of values, and proceed stage by stage; the maximum principle will start the investigation by computing one optimum path along the m-stages and then proceed to improve this optimum path based on the values obtained from the preceding computation.

The numerical calculation involved in solving a problem by dynamic programming is usually carried out by a digital computer. Because the memory capacity of a computer is limited, the data points of a variable to be searched are limited to a certain number. The point which falls between two searched points is obtained by interpolation. The errors thus introduced in interpolation are usually neither negligible nor easy to estimate. The storage difficulty becomes serious when the dimension of the state vector increases, since the memory requirement increases exponentially with the dimension [3]. Suppose that we are dealing with a problem with three variables and we are using a grid of 100 points for each variable. The total number of data points to be searched and stored is $100^3 = 1,000,000$. The task of tabulating the calculated results for 10^6 data points is, of course, difficult. Finally, the optimal policy is determined by the table entry technique using all the dynamic programming tables thus constructed. Again, the point which falls between two searched points is obtained by interpolation. One cannot fully realize the amount of labor involved in the interpolation of a function with three variables unless he has tried it.

As we have seen in previous chapters, these difficulties do not arise in the maximum principle.

The difficulty arising from the limited memory capacity of a computer becomes even more serious when the process to be optimized is a complex one. Because of the widespread occurrence of complex processes, there is an increasing interest in the study of their optimization. Using the technique of dynamic programming, Dranoff et al. [8] examined the countercurrent flow process, and Mitten and Nemhauser [9] investigated the feedback loop. An alternative algorithm, based on dynamic programming, for optimizing the feedback loop was presented by Aris [6].

The recurrence relations derived for these complex processes by dynamic programming generally include one or more additional parameters than those for the simple processes. The number of additional parameters thus introduced depends on the complexity of the process. The increase in dimensionality arises from the fact that the method of exhaustive search is used jointly with the principle of optimality in the derivation of the recurrence relations. The method of exhaustive search is employed to take care of the process streams other than the main stream. Now let us examine the difficulty in computer storage due to the increase in dimensionality. Suppose that, because of introducing a recycle stream, one additional parameter is added to the process which originally has three state variables. Assuming that a grid of 100 data points for each variable or parameter is used, we need to search and store (or tabulate) 10^8 data points!

It must be admitted that, in solving an optimization problem by the maximum principle, the difficulty in storage is avoided at the cost of introducing the covariant variables z. The values of x^N or z^N must be guessed before starting the computation. In dealing with the complex process by the maximum principle, the number of x^N or z^N to be guessed is increased. This is correspondent to the increase in dimensionality in dynamic programming. However, the increase in the number of guesses will simply increase the computing time linearly. Consequently, as long as the computer memory capacity is limited, the advantage of the maximum principle cannot be overemphasized.

Nevertheless, the definite and significant advantage of dynamic programming in the optimization of processes with constraints on state variables cannot be neglected. In the field of process control, a few attempts [10 through 14], based on the maximum principle, have been made to derive an algorithm applicable to processes with bounded state variables. However, the resulting formulations become, in general, very complicated when they are applied in solving an optimization problem numerically. The processes with bounded state variables do not give any trouble to the method of dynamic programming since, in this method, the optimal decisions are determined for the whole allowable domain of the state variables, and hence the optimal policy thus obtained automatically satisfies the constraints on the state variables.

Because of the elegant simplicity and versatility of the "principle of optimality," the method of dynamic programming can be used to handle the processes for which the transformation at each stage is difficult to be expressed in finite difference equations and thus is verbally described. The maximum principle, on the other hand, is applicable only to the processes with well-defined performance equations, and the transformation functions must be continuously differentiable with respect to the state variables.

If an optimization problem has several local optimal policies, there is no assurance that the optimal policy found by the maximum principle is the global optimal policy. Since the method of dynamic programming employs the so-called imbedding technique, which is in its spirit similar to the exhaustive search, the optimal policy obtained is always the global optimal policy provided that the interpolation error inherent to the method is negligible.

It may be proposed that, when an accurate solution is desired or required, the method of dynamic programming be employed first to locate approximately the position of global maximum and then the maximum principle be applied to pinpoint the maximum point.

Another salient feature associated with the method of dynamic programming, which is not found in the maximum principle, is the fact that the dynamic programming method can be used to determine not only the optimal but also the suboptimal policies for systems with finite number of decisions. This point is elaborated in detail in Appendix 3.

REFERENCES

1. Lee, E. S., "Optimum Design and Operation of Chemical Processes," *Ind. Eng. Chem.*, **55**, No. 8, 37 (1963).
2. Rozonoer, L. I., "The Maximum Principle of L. S. Pontryagin in Optimal-system Theory," *Automat. Telemech.*, *Moscow*, **20**, 1320, 1441, 1561 (1959). English translation in *Automation and Remote Control*, **20**, 1288, 1405, 1517 (1960).
3. Chang, S. S. L., "Dynamic Programming and Pontryagin's Maximum Principle," *Proceedings of Dynamic Programming Workshop*, (Second Annual Pre-JACC Workshop), pp. 109–183, Boulder, Colorado, June 1961.
4. Leitmann, G., *Optimization Techniques*, Academic Press, New York 1962.
5. Lapidus, L., "Dynamic Optimization and Stability," a paper presented at the Buffalo Meeting of A.I.Ch.E., May 1963.
6. Aris, R., *Discrete Dynamic Programming*, Blaisdell Publishing Co., New York, 1963.
7. Lee, E. S., "Optimization by Pontryagin's Maximum Principle on the Analog Computer," pp. 524–531, preprints of papers, *JACC*, June 1963.
8. Dranoff, J. S., L. G. Mitten, W. F. Stevens, and L. A. Wanninger, Jr., "Application of Dynamic Programming to Counter-current Flow Processes," *Operations Research*, **9**, 388 (1961).
9. Mitten, L. G. and G. L. Nemhauser, "Multistage Optimization with Dynamic Programming," a paper presented at the Los Angeles Meeting of A.I.Ch.E., February 1962. See also "Multistage Optimization," *Chem. Engg. Prog.*, **59**, 52 (1963).
10. Pontryagin, L. S., V. G. Boltyanskii, R. V. Gamkrelidze, and E. F. Mishchenko, *The Mathematical Theory of Optimal Processes*, English translation by K. N. Trirogoff, Interscience Publishers, New York, 1962.
11. Gamkrelidze, R. V., "Time Optimal Processes with Bounded Phase Coordinates," *Pokl. Akad. Nauk SSSR*, **125**, 275–478 (1959).
12. Gamkrelidze, R. V., "Optimal Control Processes with Restricted Phase Coordinates," *Bull. Acad. Sci. U.R.S.S. Ser. Mat.*, **24**, 315 (1960).
13. Chang, S. S. L., "Optimal Control in Bounded Phase Space," *AFOSR Report* 1238 (1961).
14. Chang, S. S. L., "An Extension of Ascoli's Theorem and Its Application to the Theory of Optimal Control," *AFOSR Report* 1973 (1962).

Pontryagin's Maximum Principle

In this appendix, the basic notion of the original version of Pontryagin's maximum principle [1] is outlined. It can be used to treat a wide variety of optimization problems associated with continuous processes. In order to bring out the main features, we shall restrict our discussion to the continuous processes whose performance equations are of the form

$$\frac{dx_i(\tau)}{d\tau} = f_i[x_1(\tau), \ldots, x_s(\tau); \theta_1(\tau), \ldots, \theta_t(\tau)], \qquad i = 1, 2, \ldots, s$$

or in vector form

$$\frac{dx(\tau)}{d\tau} = f[x(\tau); \theta(\tau)] \tag{1}$$

where $x(\tau)$ is an s-dimensional vector function representing the state of the process at time τ, and $\theta(\tau)$ is a t-dimensional vector function representing the decision at time τ. It may be noted that the variable τ may represent the distance in a steady-state spacewise continuous process.

A basic optimization problem associated with such a process is to choose a piecewise continuous decision vector function $\theta(\tau)$ subject to the constraints

$$\phi_i[\theta_1(\tau), \ldots, \theta_t(\tau)] \leq 0, \qquad i = 1, 2, \ldots, m \tag{2}$$

so as to minimize a linear functional of the final values of the state

$$S = \sum_{i=1}^{s} c_i x_i(T), \qquad c_i = \text{constant} \tag{3}$$

with the initial condition $x(\tau_0) = x^0$ given. The decision vector function so chosen is called an optimal decision and denoted as $\overline{\theta(\tau)}$. There are two different types of problem: a fixed right-end problem and a free right-end problem, depending on whether the final condition is given or not. Here we shall consider only the free right-end problem.

To solve this problem, we introduce a covariant vector function $z(\tau)$ and a Hamiltonian function H satisfying the following relations:

$$H[z(\tau), x(\tau), \theta(\tau)] = \sum_{i=1}^{s} z_i f_i[x(\tau); \theta(\tau)] \tag{4}$$

$$\frac{dz_i(\tau)}{d\tau} = - \frac{\partial H[z(\tau), x(\tau), \theta(\tau)]}{\partial x_i(\tau)}, \qquad i = 1, 2, \ldots, s \tag{5}$$

$$z_i(T) = -c_i, \qquad i = 1, 2, \ldots, s \tag{6}$$

It can be seen that once the decision vector function $\theta(\tau)$ is chosen, the covariant vector function $z(\tau)$ is uniquely determined by equations (5) and (6) and the initial condition $x(\tau_0) = x^0$. It may also be noted that the performance equations may be rewritten in terms of the Hamiltonian function as

$$\frac{dx_i(\tau)}{d\tau} = \frac{\partial H[z(\tau), x(\tau), \theta(\tau)]}{\partial z_i(\tau)}, \qquad i = 1, 2, \ldots, s \tag{7}$$

Then the optimal decision is the decision vector function that maximizes* the Hamiltonian function for every τ, $\tau_0 \leq \tau \leq T$.

Thus Pontryagin's maximum principle can be summarized in the following theorem.

THEOREM. Let $\theta(\tau)$, $\tau_0 \leq \tau \leq T$ be a piecewise continuous vector function satisfying the constraints given in equation (2). In order that the scalar functional S given in equation (3) be minimum for a process described by equation (7), with the initial condition $x(\tau_0) = x^0$ given, it is necessary that there exists a nonzero continuous vector function $z(\tau)$ satisfying equations (5) and (6), and that the vector function $\theta(\tau)$ be so chosen that

$$H[z(\tau), x(\tau), \theta(\tau)] = \text{maximum for every } \tau, \tau_0 \leq \tau \leq T$$

This theorem can be readily extended to cover a wide variety of problems by the techniques similar to those presented in Chapter 3.

To illustrate the use of Pontryagin's maximum principle, let us consider a simple example [2].

---

* It should be noted that the Hamiltonian function must be *maximized* when the objective function S is to be *minimized*. This arises from the fact that the final conditions of z_i given in equation (6) are equal to the negative values of c_i, whereas in the discrete maximum principle they are equal to the positive values of c_i.

Let it be required to find the decision function $\theta(\tau)$, which minimizes the integral $\dfrac{1}{2}\displaystyle\int_0^T [(x_1)^2 + (\theta)^2]\,d\tau$ for a process described by the performance equation

$$\frac{dx_1}{d\tau} = -ax_1 + \theta, \qquad x_1(0) = 0 \tag{8}$$

Introducing an additional state variable $x_2(\tau) = \dfrac{1}{2}\displaystyle\int_0^\tau [(x_1)^2 + (\theta)^2]\,d\tau$, we obtain the following performance equation:

$$\frac{dx_2}{d\tau} = \tfrac{1}{2}(x_1)^2 + \tfrac{1}{2}(\theta)^2, \qquad x_2(0) = 0 \tag{9}$$

The function which must be minimized is $S = x_2(T)$, that is, $c_1 = 0$, $c_2 = 1$ in equation (3). According to equations (4) through (6), we write

$$H(z, x, \theta) = -az_1x_1 + \tfrac{1}{2}z_2(x_1)^2 + z_1\theta + \tfrac{1}{2}z_2(\theta)^2 \tag{10}$$

$$\frac{dz_1}{d\tau} = az_1 - z_2x_1, \qquad z_1(T) = 0 \tag{11}$$

$$\frac{dz_2}{d\tau} = 0, \qquad z_2(T) = -1 \tag{12}$$

It immediately follows from equation (12) that $z_2 = -1$ for every τ. Thus the Hamiltonian function can be rewritten as

$$H = -az_1x_1 - \tfrac{1}{2}(x_1)^2 + z_1\theta - \tfrac{1}{2}(\theta)^2 \tag{13}$$

According to the maximum principle, the function H must be maximum in θ with the values of x and z considered as fixed. Putting $\partial H/\partial\theta = 0$, we find $\theta(\tau) = z_1(\tau)$. Substituting this expression of $\theta(\tau)$ into equation (8), we obtain

$$\frac{dx_1}{d\tau} = -ax_1 + z_1 \tag{14}$$

Substituting $z_2 = -1$ into equation (11) gives

$$\frac{dz_1}{d\tau} = x_1 + az_1 \tag{15}$$

The functions $x_1(\tau)$ and $z_1(\tau)$ are readily obtained from equations (14) and (15) with boundary conditions $x_1(0) = x^0$ and $z_1(T) = 0$. The results are

$$x_1(\tau) = A_1 e^{\lambda\tau} + A_2 e^{-\lambda\tau}$$
$$z_1(\tau) = A_3 e^{\lambda\tau} + A_4 e^{-\lambda\tau}$$

where $\lambda = \sqrt{a^2 + 1}$, $A_3 = (a + \lambda)A_1$, and $A_4 = (a - \lambda)A_2$. The constants A_1 and A_2 depend on x^0. Since $\theta(\tau) = z_1(\tau)$, the optimal decision is

$$\theta(\tau) = A_3 e^{\lambda\tau} + A_4 e^{-\lambda\tau}$$

REFERENCES

1. Pontryagin, L. S., V. G. Boltyanskii, R. V. Gamkrelidze, and E. F. Mishchenko, *The Mathematical Theory of Optimal Processes*, English translation by K. N. Trirogoff, Interscience, New York, 1962.
2. Rozonoer, L. I., "L. S. Pontryagin's Maximum Principle in the Theory of Optimum System I," *Automation and Remote Control*, **20**, 1288 (1959).

APPENDIX *2*

Dynamic Programming

Before describing the principal notions of dynamic programming, we shall introduce briefly the terminology which is frequently used in this method.

(1) State variable x, (2) decision variable D, and (3) transformation T are the same as those defined in Chapter 1, except that decision variable

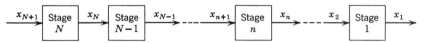

Fig. 1 Schematic representation of multistage process.

is denoted by θ in the maximum-principle algorithm. (4) Objective function is a function of state variables and/or decision variables, which is to be maximized or minimized. It is equal to the sum of the (5) interval profits, each of which is the profit from each stage and can be expressed as a function of the state variables entering that stage and the decision made at that stage. The sequence of decisions, which yields the maximum or minimum value of the objective function, is called the optimal policy.

A multistage decision process is schematically represented in Fig. 1. (The stages are numbered backwards for convenience.) For simplicity we shall consider an N-stage process characterized by only one state variable x. The transformation and the interval profit at each stage are represented by $T(x, D)$ and $P(x, D)$ respectively. The following shows how the optimal policy for such a process can be found by dynamic programming.

The method of dynamic programming is based on the principle of optimality which was stated by Bellman [1] as

An optimal policy has the property that whatever the initial state and initial decision are, the remaining decisions must constitute an optimal policy with regard to the state resulting from the first decision.

If we consider the stage n as the initial stage at which a decision is to be made, and define a function

$f_{n-1}(x) =$ the value of the objective function for the last $(n-1)$ stages when the optimal policy is followed and when the state of the stream entering the stage $(n-1)$ is x,

then it follows from the principle of optimality that

$$f_n(x) = \max_m \{f_{n-1}[T(x, D_m)] + P_n(x, D_m)\} \tag{1}$$

This means that the optimal decision at the stage n is one that makes the sum of $f_{n-1}[T(x, D)]$ and $P_n(x, D)$ maximum. Since the states of the process stream at all intermediate stages are unknown before the problem is completely solved, the functional equation cannot become immediately useful in solving an n-stage optimization problem. To overcome this difficulty, we employ the so-called imbedding technique which can be carried out in two steps. The first step is to construct a table for each stage, relating the optimal decisions to the corresponding values of the objective function for each possible value of the state variable entering each stage. The second step is to determine the optimal policy for the entire process by means of the table entry technique utilizing all the tables constructed.

In constructing the tables, we start from the last stage, proceeding backwards to the initial stage. In each step of construction, the stage for which the table is to be constructed is considered as the initial stage. For example, if we are constructing the table for the stage n, it is taken as the initial stage, whereas all the downstream stages are considered as an $(n-1)$-stage process for which the maximum values of the objective functions denoted as $f_{n-1}[T(x, D)]$ are already obtained and listed in the table constructed for the stage $(n-1)$ for the different values of the entering state variable. By means of equation (1) and the table of the stage $(n-1)$, we can obtain the optimal decision at the stage n for each possible value of the state variable entering that stage. The decisions so obtained and the corresponding value of the function $f_n(x)$ are listed in a table, which is then used to construct the table for the preceeding stage. To construct the table for stage 1, $f_0(x)$ are taken as zero. It may be noted that because we can compute the function $f_n(x)$ for only a finite number of allowable values of x, the method of interpolation must be used to obtain the values of $f_n(x)$ for the x which falls between two neighboring values of x listed in the table.

The construction of such a table and the use of the table entry technique will be illustrated in the numerical example presented in Appendix 3, where both the optimal and suboptimal policies are considered simultaneously.

REFERENCE

1. Bellman, R., *Dynamic Programming*, Princeton Univ. Press, New Jersey, 1957.

APPENDIX *3*

The kth Best Policy

It is natural that, whenever possible, the optimal policy should be used. However, it is important to prepare the best alternative to the optimal policy for the immediate adoption when the optimal policy is inaccessible. Furthermore, a knowledge of the structure of the optimal and suboptimal, that is, second best, third best . . . , policies will give us a better understanding of the process. The determination of suboptimal policies also has significance in connection with sensitivity analysis in the numerical solution of an optimization problem. To solve a problem numerically, finite difference approximation is used together with digital computers. Owing to the limited memory capacities of computers, we are often forced to use coarse grids of variables. Under this situation, a study of the neighborhood of the optimal policy can facilitate the evaluation of the meaningfulness of the solution. Thus a significant difference between the optimal and suboptimal policies may tell us that the approximation is too crude. If the suboptimal policies differ slightly from the optimal policy, we are assured that the solution is reliable.

Based on the principle of optimality, Bellman and Kalaba [1] presented an elegant method to obtain the suboptimal policies. Recently, a detailed computational technique, which may be employed in applying the mentioned method to practical problems, was established by the authors [2]. In this Appendix, the detailed computational technique is presented and illustrated by a simple directed network problem. An example in the optimal design of a multistage process with parallel redundancy is worked out in detail to show how such a technique can be applied to practical problems.

1. THE ALGORITHM

For a multistage decision process (see Fig. 1 in Appendix 2) in which the state of the process stream is transformed at each stage according to the decision made at that stage, a typical optimization problem is to determine the decision at each stage, subject to certain constraints, so that a certain function associated with the process, called the objective function of the process, is maximized.

The kth best policy is defined as the sequence of decisions which gives the objective function a value which is smaller than all those values given by first, second, . . . , $(k - 1)$th best policies, but is at least as great as the values of the objective functions given by all other suboptimal policies, that is, $(k + 1)$th, $(k + 2)$th, ...

The algorithm given below can be used to determine the first k best policies, all at a time, for the processes with a finite number of allowable decisions at each stage.

Let us first introduce the following notations:

D_m = the set of allowable decisions

$P_n(x, D_n)$ = the interval profit at stage n with the state of the entering stream x and the decision D_n

$F_N = \sum_{n=1}^{N} P_n(x, D_n)$ = the objective function for an N-stage process

$T(x, D_n)$ = transformation of the state x resulting from the decision D_n

$\max_k \{y_m\}$ = the kth largest value of the quantities y_m, $m = 1, 2, \ldots$

$f_n^{(k)}(x)$ = the value of the objective function for an n-stage process when the kth best policy is followed and the state of the stream entering the initial stage is x

$f_n^{i,j} = \max_j \{f_{n-1}^{(i)}[T(x, D_m)] + P_n(x, D_m)\}$

To determine the optimal and suboptimal policies all at a time, we make a straightforward extension of the principle of optimality as follows [2].

The kth best policy has the property that, whatever the initial state and decision are, the remaining decisions must be one of those sequences of decisions which will constitute the first k best policies with regard to the state resulting from the initial decision.

Thus, by means of this principle the decision at each stage in a process following the kth best policy can be determined one by one, starting from the last stage. If we consider a certain stage at which a decision is to be made as the initial stage, it follows from the stated principle that only the first k best policies for the remaining part of the process need to be considered in determining the decision at the stage under consideration.

Since the states of the process stream at all intermediate stages are unknown before the problem is completely solved, the stated principle cannot be applied directly. The so-called imbedding technique is employed to circumvent this difficulty. Two steps are involved in solving a problem. The first step is to construct a table for each stage, relating the decisions to the corresponding values of the objective function for each possible value of the state of the stream entering that stage. The second step is to determine the optimal and suboptimal policies by means of the table entry technique utilizing all the tables constructed. The procedure in constructing the tables will be considered in this section, whereas the table entry technique is to be illustrated in later sections.

The construction of the tables is started from the last stage, proceeding backwards to the initial stage. In each step of construction, the stage, for example, the stage n, for which the table is to be constructed, is considered as the initial stage. The interval profit from stage n is calculated and denoted as $P_n(x, D_m)$ for all allowable decisions and possible values of the state of the stream entering this stage. All the downstream stages are considered as an $(n - 1)$-stage process. The kth highest value of the objective function for this $(n - 1)$-stage process, denoted as $f_{n-1}^{(k)}[T(x, D_m)]$, are already obtained and listed in the tables constructed previously. It may be noted that, because of the limited memory capacities of computers, we can compute and store the function $f_{n-1}^{(k)}(x)$ for only a limited number of allowable values of x. Therefore, in using the values of $f_{n-1}^{(k)}(x)$ in constructing the table for the preceding stage, the linear interpolation is employed to obtain the value of $f_{n-1}^{(k)}(x)$ for the x which falls between two neighboring values of x listed in the table.

The decision at stage n for the n-stage process following the kth best policy is the decision which yields the kth highest value of the sum of $f_{n-1}^{(i)}[T(x, D_m)]$ and $P_n(x, D_m)$, which is denoted as $f_n^{(k)}(x)$ according to our notation. The decisions and the corresponding values of $f_n^{(k)}(x)$ thus obtained are then tabulated in a table. This table is then used to construct the table for the preceding stage. To construct the table for stage 1, $f_0^{(k)}(x)$ are taken as zero.

Since the decision at the stage n for the kth best policy is that which gives $f_n^{(k)}(x)$, the technical problem is to find the $f_n^{(k)}(x)$ from all possible values of the objective function. The following is a convenient way to carry it out.

1. Compute $f_n^{i,j}$.
2. Construct the following ordered array:

$$[f_n^{i,j}] = \begin{bmatrix} f_n^{1,1} & f_n^{1,2} & f_n^{1,3} & \cdots \\ f_n^{2,1} & f_n^{2,2} & f_n^{2,3} & \cdots \\ f_n^{3,1} & f_n^{3,2} & f_n^{3,3} & \cdots \\ \cdot & \cdot & \cdot & \cdots \\ \cdot & \cdot & \cdot & \cdots \\ \cdot & \cdot & \cdot & \cdots \end{bmatrix}$$

3. $f_n^{(k)}(x)$ is then determined as the kth largest element in $[f_n^{i,j}]$, that is, $f_n^{(k)}(x) = \max_{k}\{f_n^{i,j}\}$. This can be conveniently carried out as follows. Let $[f_{n,k}^{i,j}]$ be the remaining ordered array obtained by eliminating from $[f_n^{i,j}]$ all the elements that constitute $f_n^{(1)}(x), f_n^{(2)}(x), \ldots, f_n^{(k-1)}(x)$. Then

$$f_n^{(k)}(x) = \max_{i,j} \{\text{elements of } [f_{n,k}^{i,j}]\}$$

To determine the maximum element in $[f_{n,k}^{i,j}]$, the first elements of each row in $[f_{n,k}^{i,j}]$ are compared down to the row whose first element is $f^{i,1}$. This procedure can be verified as follows.

The elements of the ordered array have the following two properties.

1. $f_n^{i,1} \geq f_n^{i,2} \geq f_n^{i,3} \cdots, \qquad i = 1, 2, 3, \ldots$

2. $f_n^{1,1} \geq f_n^{2,1} \geq f_n^{3,1} \cdots$

The first property follows directly from the definition of $f_n^{i,j}$. The second property can be obtained by noting that

$$\max_{m}{}_1 \{f_{N-1}^{(1)}[T(x, D_m)] + P_N(x, D_m)\} \geq \{f_{N-1}^{(1)}[T(x, D^{2,1})] + P_N(x, D^{2,1})\}$$

$$\geq \max_{m}{}_1 \{f_{N-1}^{(2)}[T(x, D_m)] + P_N(x, D_m)\}$$

where $D^{2,1}$ represents the decision made at the Nth stage, which may give rise to $f^{2,1}$, and thus it is identical to one of the possible D_m selected in the last expression of the inequality relation just given.

Hence we have $f_n^{1,1} \geq f_n^{2,1}$. Similarly, we can show that $f_n^{2,1} \geq f_n^{3,1}$, $f_n^{3,1} \geq f_n^{4,1}, \ldots$. This leads to the second property.

It follows from the first property that, to determine the maximum element in $[f_{n,k}^{i,j}]$, we need to compare only the first elements of each row in $[f_{n,k}^{i,j}]$. From the second property we see that, in comparing the first elements of each row, we need not go below the row whose first element is $f^{i,1}$. Thus the labor of comparison required to determine the first kth maxima is greatly reduced.

2. A DIRECTED NETWORK

The use of the computational scheme just presented is illustrated with the directed network depicted in Fig. 1. The numbers shown on the lines are their lengths which, in general, correspond to the profits produced by the decisions represented by the lines and their directions. It is desired to find the first four best policies which yield the first four highest profits.

As in determining the optimal policy according to the principle of optimality, the calculation is started from the last stage which may be considered as a one-stage process.

For a one-stage process including only the last stage of the three-stage process under consideration, the following dynamic programming table

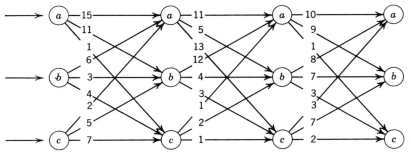

Fig. 1   A directed network.

(Table 1) can be constructed immediately from Fig. 1 without the aid of the ordered array $[f_1^{i,j}]$.

Table 1

$x_2{}^a$	D_1	$f_1^{(1)}(x_2)$	D_1	$f_1^{(2)}(x_2)$	D_1	$f_1^{(3)}(x_2)$
a	$a \rightarrow a$	10	$a \rightarrow b$	9	$a \rightarrow c$	1
b	$b \rightarrow a$	8	$b \rightarrow b$	7	$b \rightarrow c$	3
c	$c \rightarrow b$	7	$c \rightarrow a$	5	$c \rightarrow c$	2

^{a}In all the tables given in this section, the subscripts of x and D denote the stage numbers.

For a two-stage process including the last two stages of the three-stage process under consideration, the calculation is carried out for the initial state $x = a$ in the following table.

D_2	$P_2(x_3, D_2)$	$f_1^{(1)}[T(x_3, D_2)]$ $+ P_2(x_3, D_2)$	$f_1^{(2)}[T(x_3, D_2)]$ $+ P_2(x_3, D_2)$	$f_1^{(3)}[T(x_3, D_2)]$ $+ P_2(x_3, D_2)$
$a \rightarrow a$	11	21	20	12
$a \rightarrow b$	5	13	12	8
$a \rightarrow c$	13	20	18	15

The corresponding $[f_2^{i,j}]$ array is

$$\begin{bmatrix} 21 & 20 & 13 \\ 20 & 18 & 12 \\ 15 & 12 & 8 \end{bmatrix}$$

The first four highest $f_2^{i,j}$ can be obtained immediately from the preceding array. Similarly, we can find $f_2^{i,j}$ for $x = b$ and c. Such results for the two-stage process are summarized in Table 2, where i represents the number i in $f_{n-1}^{(i)}[T(x, D_n)]$, which is involved in computing $f_n^{(k)}(x)$.

Table 2

x_3	D_2	$f_2^{(1)}(x_3)$	i	D_2	$f_2^{(2)}(x_3)$	i	D_2	$f_2^{(3)}(x_3)$	i	D_2	$f_2^{(4)}(x_3)$	i
a	$a \to a$	21	1	$a \to c$ $a \to a$	20	1 2	$a \to c$	18	2	$a \to c$	15	3
b	$b \to a$	22	1	$b \to a$	21	2	$b \to a$	13	3	$b \to b$	12	1
c	$c \to a$	11	1	$c \to b$ $c \to a$	10	1 2	$c \to b$	9	2	$c \to c$	8	1

The calculation for the three-stage process is similar to the one for the two-stage process. The $[f_3^{i,j}]$ array for the initial state $x = a$ and the results for the three-stage process follow.

$$\begin{bmatrix} 36 & 33 & 12 \\ 35 & 32 & 11 \\ 33 & 24 & 10 \\ 30 & 23 & 9 \end{bmatrix}$$

Table 3

x_4	D_3	$f_3^{(1)}(x_4)$	i	D_3	$f_3^{(2)}(x_4)$	i	D_3	$f_3^{(3)}(x_4)$	i	D_3	$f_3^{(4)}(x_4)$	i
a	$a \to a$	36	1	$a \to a$	35	2	$a \to a$ $a \to b$	33	3 1	$a \to b$	32	2
b	$b \to a$	27	1	$b \to a$	26	2	$b \to b$	25	1	$b \to b$ $b \to a$	24	2 3
c	$c \to b$	27	1	$c \to b$	26	2	$c \to a$	23	1	$c \to a$	22	2

The first four highest profits for the whole process can be obtained from Table 3. The corresponding optimal and suboptimal policies are then determined by the table entry technique utilizing Tables 1 through 3.

For example, the optimal policy is obtained as follows. Starting from Table 3, we find $f_3^{(1)}(a) = 36$ with $D_3 = a \rightarrow a$, $x_3 = a$ and $i = 1$. With these values, we find from Table 2 that $D_2 = a \rightarrow a$, $x_2 = a$ and $i = 1$. Similarly, from Table 1 we find $D_1 = a \rightarrow a$. The optimal and suboptimal policies so obtained are summarized in Table 4.

Table 4

Profit	Path
First highest $\quad = 36$	$a \rightarrow a \rightarrow a \rightarrow a$
Second highest $= 35$	$a \rightarrow a \rightarrow c \rightarrow b$
	$\searrow a \rightarrow b$
Third highest $\quad = 33$	$a \rightarrow a \rightarrow c \rightarrow a$
	$\searrow b \rightarrow a \rightarrow a$
Fourth highest $= 32$	$a \rightarrow b \rightarrow a \rightarrow b$

This simple example is used for the purpose of illustration. The algorithm can be easily written in a computer program to solve many practical and complicated problems. It is found that the computation time required for determining the first few best policies is only slightly longer than that required for determining the optimal policy alone.

3. A MULTISTAGE PROCESS WITH PARALLEL REDUNDANCY

The following example shows the application of the algorithm to the optimal design of a multistage process with parallel redundancy [3]. Figure 2 shows a multistage process in which a primary raw material is reacted with a secondary specie in the initial stage to produce an intermediate product which is then fed to the next stage and reacted with another secondary specie and so on through the entire process. Suppose that the secondary species are all quite unstable and cannot be stored and therefore must be produced on demand by special reactions. All the intermediate products are also assumed to be unstable. Then it is clear that if a secondary specie is not available on time at any stage, the entire processing system will fail.

Such a failure is a stochastic phenomenon and therefore can be considered from a probabilistic point of view. The probability that the nth secondary specie will be available on time is called the reliability of stage n and represented by R_n. The reliability of the whole process R is the probability that all the N secondary species are available on time and thus

$$R = \prod_{n=1}^{N} R_n$$

If the process which produces a certain secondary specie fails frequently, it would be desirable to produce more than one batch of that specie to increase the probability that it will be available on time. The production of more than one batch to reduce the effects of failure is named the parallel redundancy.

Suppose that b_n batches of the nth secondary specie are prepared. Since only one batch is needed, $(b_n - 1)$ batches are redundant. The probability

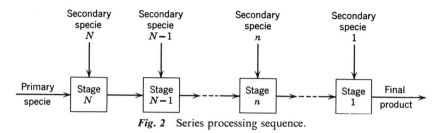

Fig. 2 Series processing sequence.

that all b_n batches will fail is equal to $(1 - R_n)^{b_n}$. Hence the probability that at least one batch will succeed is $[1 - (1 - R_n)^{b_n}]$ which is by definition the reliability of stage n with its redundancies. Thus the reliability of the entire process with redundancy can be represented by

$$R = \prod_{n=1}^{N} [1 - (1 - R_n)^{b_n}] \tag{1}$$

Since $b_n \geq 1$ and $R_n \leq 1$, it can be shown that

$$[1 - (1 - R_n)^{b_n}] \geq R_n$$

which indicates that the reliability of the process is increased by the use of the parallel redundancy.

Let P_g be the unit price of the final product. The expected profit for the system is then expressed by $P_g R$. Let C_n be the construction cost of one reactor for the production of the nth secondary specie (the cost is properly distributed over the life of the process) and O_n be the operating cost. Then the net profit for the entire process P is

$$P = P_g R - \sum_{n=1}^{N} (C_n + O_n) b_n \tag{2}$$

The optimal parallel redundancy is the design which maximizes P given in equation (2). Rudd [4] has applied the method of dynamic programming in the optimal design for such a process. Now let us use the algorithm described in Section 1 to find the first four best designs, all at a time.

For definiteness, we shall consider a three-stage process with the following data:

	C_n	O_n	R_n for One Batch
Stage 3	0.1	0.1	$\frac{1}{3}$
Stage 2	0.5	0.5	$\frac{1}{2}$
Stage 1	0.5	0.5	$\frac{3}{4}$

The unit price associated with the final product P_g is 10 units. Now, if P in equation (2) is considered as the objective function, R in equation (1) as the state variable, and b_n as decision, the following relations can be obtained:

$$f_1^{1,j} = \max_{b_1} \{10x_1 - b_1\}, \qquad b_1 = 1, 2, \ldots \tag{3}$$

$$x_1 = x_2[1 - (\tfrac{1}{4})^{b_1}] \tag{4}$$

$$f_2^{i,j} = \max_{b_2} \{f_1^i(x_2) - b_2\}, \qquad b_2 = 1, 2, \ldots \tag{5}$$

$$x_2 = x_3[1 - (\tfrac{1}{2})^{b_2}] \tag{6}$$

$$f_3^{i,j} = \max_{b_3} \{f_2^i(x_3) - 0.2 \cdot b_3\}, \qquad b_3 = 1, 2, \ldots \tag{7}$$

$$x_3 = x_4[1 - (\tfrac{2}{3})^{b_3}] = 1 - (\tfrac{2}{3})^{b_3} \tag{8}$$

Here x_n is the reliability of the process consisting of stage n and all upstream stages. Since the primary specie is assumed to be always available, $x_4 = 1$.

For the one-stage process consisting of stage 1 only, we have

$$f_1^{(k)}(x) = f_1^{1,k}$$

This can be readily obtained and therefore the construction of the ordered array of $f_1^{i,j}$ is not necessary. A portion of the numerical results is given in Table 5.

Table 5

x_2	$f_1^{(1)}(x_2)$	b_1	$f_1^{(2)}(x_2)$	b_1	$f_1^{(3)}(x_2)$	b_1
0.65	4.093	2	3.875	1	3.398	3
0.70	4.562	2	4.250	1	3.890	3
0.75	5.031	2	4.625	1	4.382	3
0.80	5.500	2	5.000	1	4.875	3
0.85	5.968	2	5.375	1	5.367	3
0.90	6.437	2	5.859	3	5.750	1

For the two-stage process including stage 1 and stage 2, all values of $f_2^{i,j}$ are calculated from equation (5) for each possible value of x_3. The corresponding $f_2^{i,j}$ array is then constructed. For example, the ordered array for $x_3 = 0.9$ is

$$\begin{bmatrix} 2.382 & 2.062 & \ldots & \ldots \\ 2.327 & 1.906 & \ldots & \ldots \\ 1.909 & \cdot & \ldots & \ldots \\ \cdot & \cdot & \ldots & \ldots \end{bmatrix}$$

The valuēs of $f_2^{(k)}(x_3)$ for $x_3 = 0.9$ are then obtained from this array. Similarly, we can find $f_2^{(k)}(x_3)$ for all other values of x_3. A part of the results is shown in Table 6.

Table 6

x_3	$f_2^{(1)}(x_3)$	b_2	x_2	i^a	$f_2^{(2)}(x_3)$	b_2	x_2	i
0.90	2.382	3	0.7875	1	2.327	2	0.6750	1
0.95	2.792	3	0.8312	1	2.679	2	0.7125	1
1.00	3.202	3	0.8750	1	3.031	2	0.7500	1

[a] i represents the number i in $f_{n-1}^{(i)} [T(x, D_n)]$, which is involved in computing $f_n^{(k)}(x)$.

The construction of the table for the three-stage process is similar to the one for the two-stage process. However, for the three-stage process it suffices to construct only for $x_4 = 1$. The numerical results are given in Table 7. The first four highest profits for the whole process are represented

Table 7

k	$f_3^{(k)}(x_4)$	b_3	x_3	i
1	1.322	7	0.9414	1
2	1.282	6	0.9122	1
2	1.282	8	0.9609	1
3	1.218	7	0.9414	2
4	1.212	6	0.9122	2

by those $f_3^{(k)}(x_4)$, $k = 1, 2, 3, 4$ listed in Table 7. The corresponding optimal and suboptimal policies are then determined by the table entry technique utilizing Tables 5 through 7. For example, the optimal policy is obtained as follows:

Starting from Table 7, we find $f_3^{(1)}(x_4) = 1.322$ with $b_3 = 7$, $x_3 = 0.9414$

and $i = 1$. By means of linear interpolation, the values of b_2, x_2, and i for $x_3 = 0.9414$ can be obtained from Table 6. The results are

$$b_2 = 3, \qquad x_2 = 0.8237, \qquad i = 1$$

Similarly, from Table 5 we find $b_1 = 2$. The optimal and suboptimal policies thus obtained are summarized in Table 8.

Table 8

Profit		Policies		
		b_1	b_2	b_3
First highest	= 1.322	2	3	7
Second highest	= 1.282	$\begin{cases}2 \\ 2\end{cases}$	2 3	6 8
Third highest	= 1.218	2	2	7
Fourth highest	= 1.212	2	2	6

REFERENCES

1. Bellman, R. and R. Kalaba, "On the kth Best Policy," *J. Soc. Indust. Appl. Math.*, **8,** 582 (1960).
2. Fan, L. T. and C. S. Wang, "A Note on kth Best Policies," unpublished report, July 1963.
3. Fan, L. T. and C. S. Wang, "Optimal and Suboptimal Policies for a Multistage Decision Process," unpublished report, July 1963.
4. Rudd, D. F., "Reliability Theory in Chemical System Design," *Ind. Eng. Chem. Fundamentals*, **1,** 138 (1962).

Comments on the Necessary and Sufficient Condition for Optimality

It was mentioned in Chapter 3 that the condition:

$$\frac{\partial H^n}{\partial \theta^n} = 0 \tag{1}$$

or

$$H^n = \text{maximum}, \tag{2}$$

is, in general, just a necessary condition for the optimality. This arises from the fact that in some cases, the terms $0(\epsilon^2)$ in equation (3.19) plays an important role. For the processes whose transformation functions are not linear in their arguments, a complete analysis of the sign of $0(\epsilon^2)$ is very complicated. No attempt, therefore, will be made to present such an analysis of the sufficient condition for the general case. In the following passages, we shall discuss at first the conditions for the applicability of equations (1) and (2) and then show that equation (2) is the necessary as well as the sufficient condition for the processes whose transformation functions are linear in their arguments. A simple example is included to illustrate the difference between the conditions $\partial H^n / \partial \theta^n = 0$ and $H^n = \text{maximum}$.

The condition, $\partial H^n / \partial \theta^n = 0$, is the necessary condition and applicable for a stage in which the value of $\overline{\theta^n}$ obtained from this condition lies within the admissible region of the decision variables. However, it cannot be assured that the value of $\overline{\theta^n}$ thus obtained is the one which maximizes the Hamiltonian function. It may be the one which minimizes the

Hamiltonian function. There is also a possibility that it will be an inflection point and hence will neither maximize nor minimize the Hamiltonian function. These situations are analogous to the maximization problems in differential calculus and can be readily visualized from the following equation [the same as equation (3.19)]

$$\sum_{n=1}^{N} \sum_{i=1}^{s} \sum_{j=1}^{t} z_i{}^n (\epsilon \Phi_j{}^n) \cdot \frac{\partial T_i{}^n(\overline{x^{n-1}; \theta^n})}{\partial \theta_j{}^n} + 0(\epsilon^2) \leq 0$$

or equivalently,

$$\sum_{n=1}^{N} \sum_{j=1}^{t} \epsilon \Phi_j{}^n \cdot \frac{\partial H^n}{\partial \theta_j{}^n} + 0(\epsilon^2) \leq 0 \tag{3}$$

When $\partial H^n / \partial \theta_j{}^n$ in equation (3) vanishes, the sign of the left-hand side will depend on $0(\epsilon^2)$, which may be negative, positive, or zero.

For the stage where the condition, $\partial H^n / \partial \theta^n = 0$, gives the value of $\overline{\theta^n}$ outside the admissible region, the optimal decision generally occurs at the boundary points. Since $\partial H^n / \partial \theta_j{}^n \neq 0$, the sign of the left-hand side of equation (3) will be determined completely by $\sum_{j=1}^{t} \epsilon \Phi_j{}^n \dfrac{\partial H^n}{\partial \theta_j{}^n}$ which is of the order of ϵ. It is obvious that the condition $\sum_{j=1}^{t} \epsilon \Phi_j{}^n (\partial H^n / \partial \theta_j{}^n) < 0$ is equivalent to the condition $H^n = $ maximum. Thus for this stage the optimal decision can be determined by equation (2).

For the processes whose transformation functions are linear in their arguments, that is,

$$T_i{}^n(x^{n-1}; \theta^n) = \sum_{j=1}^{s} A_{ji}{}^n x_j{}^{n-1} + \sum_{j=1}^{t} B_{ji}{}^n \theta_j{}^n$$

it can be seen that $0(\epsilon^2)$ is identically equal to zero. Thus equation (3) becomes

$$\sum_{n=1}^{N} \sum_{j=1}^{t} \epsilon \Phi_j{}^n \cdot \frac{\partial H^n}{\partial \theta_j{}^n} < 0 \quad \text{or} \quad [H^n(\overline{x^n}; \theta^n) - H^n(\overline{x^n}; \overline{\theta^n})] < 0$$

This implies that the condition, $H^n = $ maximum, is necessary as well as sufficient.

It is important to note that the condition, $\partial H^n / \partial \theta^n = 0$, is not necessarily equivalent to the condition $H^n = $ maximum. They are applicable in different situations as explained in the preceding paragraphs. It is only when the point where $\partial H^n / \partial \theta^n = 0$ is coincidently the maximum point of H^n that they are equivalent to each other. The following example, originally given by Jackson and Horn and communicated to the author by Aris [1], shows that $\partial H^n / \partial \theta^n = 0$ may occur at the maximum point of H^n in a problem in which we seek to minimize a certain objective function.

Consider a simple two-stage process with the following performance equations:

First stage

$$x_1^1 = x_1^0 - 2\theta^1 - \tfrac{1}{2}(\theta^1)^2, \qquad x_1^0 = 1$$

$$x_2^1 = x_2^0 + \theta^1, \qquad\qquad x_2^0 = 1$$

Second stage

$$x_1^2 = x_1^1 + (x_2^1)^2 + (\theta^2)^2$$

$$x_2^2 = \text{arbitrary function of } x_1^1, x_2^1, \text{ and } \theta^2.$$

It is desired to minimize x_1^2. By direct calculation, we have

$$x_1^2 = 2 + \tfrac{1}{2}(\theta^1)^2 + (\theta^2)^2$$

which has a minimum at $\theta^1 = \theta^2 = 0$. By the discrete maximum principle we have

$$z_1^2 = 1, \qquad z_2^2 = 0 \quad \text{and} \quad H^2 = x_1^1 + (x_2^1)^2 + (\theta^2)^2$$

Both conditions $\partial H^n/\partial \theta^n = 0$ and $H^n = $ minimum give the same result of $\theta^2 = 0$ as the optimal decision at the second stage. But for the first stage, we have $z_1^1 = 1$, $z_2^1 = 2x_2^1 = 2(1 + \overline{\theta^1})$
and

$$H^1 = 1 - 2\theta^1 - \tfrac{1}{2}(\theta^1)^2 + z_2^1(1 + \theta^1)$$

$$= 1 + z_2^1 + (z_2^1 - 2)\theta^1 - \tfrac{1}{2}(\theta^1)^2$$

The condition $\partial H^n/\partial \theta^n = 0$ gives $\overline{\theta^1} = z_2^1 - 2 = 2(1 + \overline{\theta^1}) - 2 = 2\overline{\theta^1}$, from which we obtain $\overline{\theta^1} = 0$. However, since $(\partial/\partial\theta^1)(\partial H^1/\partial\theta^1) = -1$, H^1 is a maximum, instead of a minimum at $\theta^1 = 0$.

REFERENCE

1. Aris, R., private communication, 1964.

Nomenclature

CHAPTER 3

c	constant in objective function
H	the Hamiltonian function
M	mixing operator
n	the nth stage
N	the Nth stage or the total number of stages
q	flow rate of the feed
r	flow rate of the recycle stream
s	total number of state variables in each stage
t	total number of decision variables in each stage
T	transformation operator
x	state vector
$\bar{x}$	the optimal value of x
x^f	the value of x of the feed stream
$\underline{x}$	an $(s + 1)$-dimensional vector
y	perturbation of the state vector
z	an s-dimensional covariant vector

Greek Letters

ϵ	a small number
θ	decision vector
$\bar{\theta}$	the optimal value of θ
σ	a parameter in the performance equation
ϕ	perturbation of the decision vector
χ	the new state variable
ω	the new decision variable

CHAPTER 4

a	constant
A	$\dfrac{\delta \rho \lambda_v C}{q C_p H}$

A_i	the ith chemical specie
b	constant
b^n	constant
c_i	constants in objective function; concentration
C	cross-sectional area of air flow channel
C^n	exhaust speed at the nth stage
C_p	specific heat of air
d^n	$(x_1^{n-1} - x_e)/v^n(T_0 - T_G^{n-1})$
E	activation energy
E^n	energy consumption at the nth stage
f	feed stream
F	mass flow rate of reaction mixture
G	performance function
G^n	flow rate of hot stream air
h	humidity
H	Hamiltonian function
k	reaction rate constant
m	flow rate of tube side material; number of moles in Section 5
M	mixing operator
n	the nth stage
N	total number of stages
P	profit
P^N	gas pressure leaving the last stage
P^0	gas pressure entering the first stage
q	flow rate of feed
Q^n	amount of heat exchanged at the nth stage
r	flow rate of feedback stream; rate of reaction in Section 3f
r^n	burnout ratio
R	gas constant
$R(x_1^n)$	maximum reaction rate
S	time
t	time of sorghum grain exposed to drying air
T	transformation operator; temperature in Section 3f
T_0	dry-bulb temperature
T_G	temperature at which the moisture of air is in equilibrium with the moisture of sorghum grain
u^n	concentration of solute in the wash water leaving the nth stage; overall heat transfer coefficient in the nth stage in Section 3d.
U^n	u^n/WC_p
V	total ideal speed
V_c	cutoff speed

v^n	$w^n/(q + r); \dfrac{G^n}{q}$
w	weight of catalyst in Section 3f
w^n	amount of wash water at the nth stage
W^n	flow rate of shell side material
$W_c{}^n$	weight of vehicle at cutoff of the nth stage
$W_0{}^n$	weight of vehicle at ignition of the nth stage
$W_s{}^n$	$W_c{}^n$ minus weight of payload of the nth stage
x	state vector
x^0	the value of the state vector entering the first stage
x^f	the value of the state vector in the feed stream
x_e	equilibrium moisture contents
z	covariant vector

Greek Letters

α	constant
α_i	stoichiometric coefficient
β	constant; order of a reaction
γ	order of a reaction
δ	mean distance of grains from the inlet point of air
δV	speed loss associated with gravity and drag
θ	decision variable
λ	relative cost of wash water or hot air
λ^n	latent heat of vaporization; payload ratio in Section 3g
λ_v	heat of vaporization of moisture in sorghum grain
ξ	conversion
ρ	bulk density of sorghum grain
ΔH	heat of reaction

CHAPTER 5

a	constant
b	constant
C	conversion of a chemical reaction
C_p	average heat capacity of the reacting mixture
F	flow rate through the reactor
$F(\theta)$	cost
H	heat of reaction
L	recycle rate
M	feed flow rate
P	profit
R	cost for regenerating or replacing catalyst
S	cumulative flow rate through the reactor

T	temperature of the product
V	value or cost
x	state vector
z	covariant vector

Greek Letters

θ	decision vector

CHAPTER 6

a	a given constant
A	a chemical specie
b	a given constant
B	a chemical specie
c	a given constant
C	a chemical specie
C_p	average heat capacity of the reaction mixture
E	activation energy
F	volumetric flow rate of the reaction mixture
$h(\theta)$	chemical reaction rate constant
H	Hamiltonian function
ΔH	heat of reaction
k	chemical reaction rate constant
$k(\theta)$	chemical reaction rate constant
K	equilibrium constant
n	the nth stage
N	total number of stages
P	a chemical specie in Section 3; net profit in Section 4
Q	a chemical specie
r	reaction rate
R	gas constant
S	time
S^n	structure coefficient
t	residence time in Section 2; temperature in Section 4
T	temperature
V	velocity in Section 1; reactor volume in Sections 2 and 4
V_a	cost of chemical specie A
V_b	cost of chemical specie B
V_h	cost for cooling
V_r	cost of unit volume of reactor
W_0^n	weight of vehicle at ignition of the nth stage
W_0^0	payload weight

x	state vector
y	conversion
Y	a chemical specie in Section 3
z	covariant vector

Greek Letters

ϵ^n	structure ratio
θ	decision vector
λ^n	payload ratio
ρ	residence time
τ	space time

CHAPTER 7

c	constant in objective function
c_i	constant
H	the Hamiltonian function
M	mixing operator
n	the nth stage
N	the Nth stage or the total number of stages
q	flow rate of the feed
r	flow rate of the recycle stream
s	total number of state variables in each stage
t	total number of decision variables in each stage
T	transformation operator
x	state vector
$\bar{x}$	the optimal value of x
y	perturbation of the state vector
z	covariant vector

Greek Letters

ϵ	a small number
θ	decision vector
$\bar{\theta}$	the optimal value of θ
ϕ	perturbation of the decision vector

APPENDIX

A	constant
b_n	number of batches for the nth secondary specie
c_i	constant
C_n	construction cost of one reactor for the nth secondary specie

D_m the set of allowable decisions
f_{n-1} the optimal value of the objective function for the last $(n - 1)$ stages
$f_n^{(k)}$ the value of the objective function for an n-stage process in the kth best policy
$f_n^{i,j}$ $\max_m \{f_{n-1}^{(i)}[T(x, D_m)] + P_n(x, D_m)\}$
F_N objective function for an N-stage process
H Hamiltonian function
P net profit of the entire process
P_g unit price of the final product
$P_n(x, D_n)$ the interval profit at stage n with a state of x and a decision D_n
R_n reliability of stage n
S the function to be minimized
$T(x, D_n)$ transformation of the state x by the decision D_n
x state vector
$x(\tau)$ state of the process at time τ
z covariant vector

Greek Letters

θ decision variable
$\theta(\tau)$ decision at time
τ time

Author Index

Subject Index